KU-126-085

CONTENTS

Introduction

The Global Warming Debate is the twenty-eighth volume in the **Issues** series. The aim of this series is to offer up-to-date information about important issues in our world.

The Global Warming Debate looks at the problem of global warming and possible solutions to it.

The information comes from a wide variety of sources and includes:
Government reports and statistics
Newspaper reports and features
Magazine articles and surveys
Literature from lobby groups
and charitable organisations.

It is hoped that, as you read about the many aspects of the issues explored in this book, you will critically evaluate the information presented. It is important that you decide whether you are being presented with facts or opinions. Does the writer give a biased or an unbiased report? If an opinion is being expressed, do you agree with the writer?

The Global Warming Debate offers a useful starting-point for those who need convenient access to information about the many issues involved. However, it is only a starting-point. At the back of the book is a list of organisations which you may want to contact for further information.

*****

The Global Warming Debate

CROYDON LIBRARIES

Nineties)

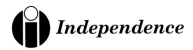

Independence

Educational Publishers
Cambridge

First published by Independence
PO Box 295
Cambridge CB1 3XP
England

British Library Cataloguing in Publication Data
The Global Warming Debate – (Issues Series)
I. Donnellan, Craig II. Series
363.7'3874

ISBN 1 86168 167 4

Printed in Great Britain
The Burlington Press
Cambridge

Typeset by
Claire Boyd

Cover
The illustration on the front cover is by
Pumpkin House.

Introduction to climate change

Information from the Atmospheric Research & Information Centre

Climate is the long-term statistical expression of short-term weather. Climate can be defined as 'expected weather'. When changes in the expected weather occur, we call these climate changes. They can be defined by the differences between average weather conditions at two separate times. Climate may change in different ways, over different time scales and at different geographical scales. In recent times, scientists have become interested in global warming, due to mankind's impact on the climate system, through the enhancement of the natural greenhouse effect.

The overall state of the global climate is determined by the amount of energy stored by the climate system, and in particular the balance between energy the Earth receives from the Sun and the energy which the Earth releases back to space, called the global energy balance. How this energy balance is regulated depends upon the flows of energy within the global climate system. Major causes of climate change involve any process that can alter the global energy balance, and the energy flows within the climate system. Causes of climate change include changes in the Earth's orbit around the Sun, changes in the amount of energy coming from the Sun, changes in ocean circulation or changes in the composition of the atmosphere. Large volcanic eruptions can affect the global climate over only a few years. By contrast, the movement of continents around the world over hundreds of millions of years can also affect global climate, but only over these much longer time scales.

Throughout the Earth's history climate has fluctuated between periods of relative warmth and relative cold. Palaeoclimatology is the study of climate and climate change prior to the period of direct measurements. Direct records of temperature and other climatic elements span only a tiny fraction of the Earth's climatic history, and so provide an inadequate perspective on climatic change and the evolution of the climate today and in the future. A longer perspective on climate variability can be obtained by the study of natural phenomena which are climate-dependent. Such phenomena provide a record of past climates, and are revealed through the study of, amongst other techniques, tree rings, ice cores and sea floor sediments.

In the last 100 years or so, the Earth's surface and lowest part of the atmosphere have warmed up on average by about 0.5°C. During this period, the amount of greenhouse gases in the atmosphere has increased, largely as a result of the burning of fossil fuels for energy and transportation, and land use changes, for food by mankind. In the last 20 years, concern has grown that these two phenomena are, at least in part, associated with each other. That is to say, global warming is now considered most probably to be due to the man-made increases in greenhouse gas emissions. Whilst other natural causes of climate change, including changes in the amount of energy coming from the Sun and shifting patterns of ocean circulation, can cause global climate to change over similar periods of time, the balance of evidence now indicates that there is a discernible human influence on the global climate.

• The above information is from the Atmospheric Research & Information Centre web site which can be found at www.doc.mmu.ac.uk/aric/

© Atmospheric Research & Information Centre (ARIC)

All you ever wanted to know about climate change

Global warming: frequently asked questions

What is the greenhouse effect?

Warmth from the Sun heats the surface of the Earth, which in turn radiates energy back out to space. Some of this outgoing radiation, which is nearly all in the infrared region of the spectrum, is trapped in the atmosphere by so-called greenhouse gases. For instance, water vapour strongly absorbs radiation with wavelengths between 4 and 7 micrometres, and carbon dioxide absorbs radiation with wavelengths between 13 and 19 micrometres.

The trapped radiation warms the lower part of the Earth's atmosphere, the troposphere. This warmed air radiates energy – again, largely in the infrared – in all directions. Some of the radiation works its way up and out of the atmosphere, but some finds its way back down to the Earth's surface, keeping it hotter than it would otherwise be. This is the greenhouse effect.

Are water and carbon dioxide all we have to worry about?

No. Other gases can absorb infrared radiation and contribute to greenhouse warming. These include methane, ozone, CFCs (chlorofluorocarbons) and nitrous oxide (released by nitrogen-based fertilisers). Of these, methane is the most important. Its concentration in the atmosphere has more than doubled since pre-industrial times. Sources of methane include the biological activity of bacteria in paddy fields and the guts of cattle, the release of natural gas from landfills and commercial oil and gas fields, and vegetation rotting in the absence of oxygen – for instance, in the depths of man-made reservoirs. Recent studies suggest this last source could be responsible for up to a fifth of global methane emissions. Molecule for molecule, other sub-stances are even more potent greenhouse gases. A single molecule of either of the two most common CFCs has the same greenhouse warming effect as 10,000 molecules of CO_2.

And the greenhouse effect is a thoroughly bad thing?

Not quite. Without it, the planet wouldn't be warm enough to support life as we know it. The problem is that beneficial natural levels of greenhouse gases in the atmosphere are being boosted by human activities, especially the burning of fossil fuels. If nothing is done to curb emissions of CO_2, for example, the amount of CO_2 in the atmosphere will probably be more than double pre-industrial levels by the end of the 21st century.

How do we know what these levels were?

The most informative measurements have come from bubbles of air trapped in Antarctic ice. These show that for at least the past 400,000 years, CO_2 levels in the atmosphere have closely followed the global temperatures as revealed in ice cores, tree rings and elsewhere.

If it's all so precise, why is there so much confusion and uncertainty about global warming? Surely if we know how much CO_2 is entering the atmosphere and how much energy each molecule can trap, we ought to be able to calculate the overall warming effect?

It's not that simple. For example there is no easy formula for predicting what future increases in CO_2 levels will do to the average global temperature. While we can calculate that a doubling of CO_2 in the atmosphere will force roughly 1°C warming, the planet is more complex than that. It could respond by magnifying the effect, but it could also conceivably damp down the warming. These feedbacks involve essential planetary

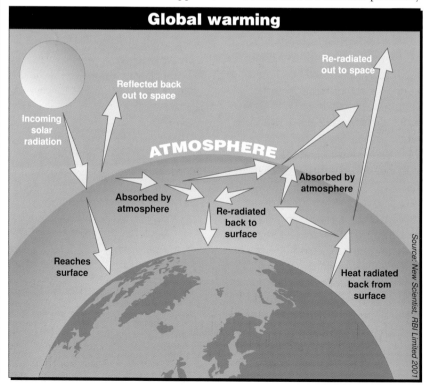

processes, such as the formation of ice, clouds, the circulation of the oceans and biological activity.

What effects are the main feedbacks likely to have?

One of the easiest effects to estimate is the 'ice-albedo' feedback. As the world warms, ice caps will melt. As this happens, water or land will replace parts of the Earth's surface that were once covered with ice. Ice is very efficient at reflecting solar radiation into space, whereas water and land absorb far more. So the Earth's surface will trap more heat, increasing warming – a positive feedback. Less clear-cut is the impact of the extra water vapour likely to enter the atmosphere because of higher evaporation rates. This added water vapour itself contributes to the greenhouse effect, another positive feedback. But it may also increase cloud cover. The dominant effect of some low-altitude clouds is to shroud and cool the Earth – a negative feedback – but other clouds, such as cirrus, may trap heat at low levels, giving another positive feedback.

Disputes about how water vapour and clouds will influence global warming are at the heart of many of the disputes between mainstream scientists and the handful of greenhouse sceptics. Overall, the majority view is that positive feedbacks could amplify the warming effect by perhaps 2.5 times. But some sceptics believe the feedback effect could be neutral or even predominantly negative.

Why do sceptical scientists think that?

One reason is that something strange has been happening to warming trends in the past couple of decades. While ground-level temperatures around the world have gone up, the warming has failed to penetrate the atmosphere. The atmosphere has actually been cooling in some large areas three kilometres above the Earth. According to computerised climate models, the warming should spread right through the troposphere, the bottom ten kilometres or so of the atmosphere. Sceptics argue that if the models are wrong about how

surface warming influences temperatures in the troposphere, they are also likely to be wrong about the movement of water vapour between the surface and the upper troposphere. That in turn may mean they are wrong about water-vapour feedback – one of the vital mechanisms behind global warming.

So does this mean there are some scientists who don't believe in the greenhouse effect or global warming?

No, this is a myth. All scientists believe in the greenhouse effect. Without it the planet would be largely frozen. And all scientists accept that if humans put more greenhouse gases in the atmosphere it will tend to warm the planet. The only disagreement is over precisely how much warming will be amplified by feedbacks. And there is a growing consensus that the average global warming of 0.6°C seen in the past century – and particularly the pronounced warming of the past two decades – is largely a consequence of the greenhouse effect.

Are there other complications?

Yes. A whole series of other feedbacks will influence the concentration of greenhouse gases in the atmosphere. Not all the CO_2 that we put into the atmosphere stays there. Some is absorbed by vegetation on land – usually forests – and some is taken up by the oceans. If the rate at which CO_2 is absorbed changes, then the rate of build-up of CO_2 in the

atmosphere will also change – speeding up or slowing down global warming. One way to increase the build-up of CO_2 would be to chop down all the tropical forests. Another could be the impact of warming on ocean currents, particularly the global 'conveyor belt' that begins in the North Atlantic. When ice forms, the remaining sea water becomes more saline and so denser. This denser water descends to the ocean floor, where it begins a long journey through the oceans that lasts an estimated thousand years. This water carries dissolved CO_2 with it on its long journey. Most oceanographers believe that as warming takes hold and ice formation is reduced, these currents could slow down or carry less water, which could mean less CO_2 is removed from the atmosphere. This is now taken into account in warming predictions.

This is all very pessimistic. Isn't it true that a warmer planet will absorb more pollution?

Yes indeed. Warmer temperatures and the fertilising effect of more CO_2 in the air will stimulate faster growth of trees and other vegetation, which in turn will help to soak up some of the CO_2 in the atmosphere. This can already be seen in some places. But plants need other things besides CO_2 to grow. They need water, which could be in short supply as greater evaporation rates will dry out soils. Plants also need space, which we are using up for urban development. They also need climatic stability. Recent studies by the Inter-governmental Panel on Climate Change (IPCC) suggest that climate change could soon be so fast that many forests, particularly in northern latitudes, will be unable to adapt and could die off – releasing their carbon into the atmosphere.

What about organisms in the oceans?

Once dissolved in surface waters, a lot of CO_2 is absorbed by plankton and other marine organisms and turned into organic compounds. Most of this eventually falls to the ocean floor. The strength of this sink for carbon depends on how much life the ocean is producing. It is not clear to what extent global warming will affect the oceans' biological productivity – it could rise or fall. Cooler seas tend to produce more life, but iron dust from expanding deserts could make warm seas more fertile. And some scientists have investigated whether we could boost this effect artificially by seeding the oceans with iron.

Anything else that could shield us from global warming?

Yes, volcanoes. When Mount Pinatubo erupted in June 1991, it threw a huge amount of debris into the stratosphere that partially shielded the surface of the Earth from incoming solar energy. Sulphate particles ejected from the volcano were particularly effective at scattering the sunlight. Computer models successfully predicted that in the short term, the debris would temporarily cool the Earth's atmosphere. The models also predicted that as the volcanic debris cleared in 1992 and 1993, average temperatures would swiftly return first to the level of the 1980s, and then, by the middle of the 1990s, to the slightly higher levels that would be expected with the ongoing build-up of greenhouse gases.

Sulphate particles? Don't we make them, too?

Right again. One of the nice ironies of this story is that burning coal and oil produces sulphate particles – which make acid rain. These particles help to shield the more industrialised countries from the full impact of global warming. In some places, such as central Europe and parts of China, they may have overwhelmed the warming, producing a net cooling. Other aerosols, such as dust from soil erosion and 'desertification', can also curb warming. But even if you find the idea of using one form of pollution to protect us from another, there is a problem. Whereas the average CO_2 molecule in the atmosphere lasts for about a century, sulphates and other aerosol molecules persist for only a few days. This means two things. First, if you turned down the power stations, the world would get much hotter within a few days. Secondly, aerosols do not accumulate in the atmosphere in the way that CO_2 does. If you carry on burning a given amount of fossil fuel, the cooling effect of the sulphates will remain constant, while the warming effect of CO_2 will keep on increasing. So sulphates are not a solution.

Will there be global warming everywhere?

Maybe not. Climate modellers admit to being very uncertain about how global warming will affect particular regions. This is because much of our weather depends on circulation patterns, which could alter in unexpected ways. Crudely, however, modellers expect many coastal regions to become wetter, while continental interiors will become drier, causing some deserts to expand. Warming will probably be greatest in polar regions, mirroring climate changes already seen this century in both the Arctic and Antarctic. Existing desert regions, notably central Asia, parts of the Middle East and the Sahel region of Africa, have already experienced some warming.

Local climate could also be altered by changes in ocean circulation. Western Europe could be particularly vulnerable. At present, it is kept exceptionally warm in winter by the Gulf Stream, which is part of the ocean conveyor belt (see 'Are there other complications?' previous page). Take that away and British weather would be like the Hudson Bay in Canada, which is at the same latitude. If the conveyor belt slackens, or the path of the Gulf Stream shifts, that is precisely what could happen. So British hopes of a climate like Bordeaux in the 21st century could be cruelly dashed!

Surely that's a bit sensationalist?

Not really. Ice cores reveal growing evidence of sudden, dramatic shifts in climate over the past 10,000 years that have occurred within a few decades as a result of 'flips' in ocean circulation. But most models suggest that the Gulf Stream won't turn off for at least another century.

Are there any other cataclysmic events in the offing?

One fear is that the entire West Antarctic and Greenland ice sheets might disappear into the oceans raising sea levels by seven metres or more. Even the most pessimistic experts say this is only a worry if the world warms by about 4°C, which is outside the range of mainstream predictions for the next century. And a glacial collapse is such a slow process it would take several hundred years for all the ice to slide into the sea.

So how worried should we be?

How lucky do you feel?

A greenhouse timeline

A greenhouse timeline from 1827 to the present

1827: French polymath Jean-Baptiste Fourier suggests the existence of an atmospheric effect keeping the Earth warmer than it would otherwise be. He also uses the analogy of a greenhouse.

1863: Irish scientist John Tyndall publishes paper describing how water vapour can be a greenhouse gas.

1890s: Swedish scientist Svante Arrhenius and an American, P.C. Chamberlain, independently consider the problems that might be caused by CO_2 building up in the atmosphere. Both scientists realise that the burning of fossil fuels could lead to global warming, but neither suspect the process might already have started.

1890s to 1940: Average surface air temperatures increase by about 0.25°C. Some scientist see the American Dust Bowl as a sign of the greenhouse effect at work.

1940 to 1970: Worldwide cooling of 0.2°C. Scientific interest in greenhouse effect wanes. Some climatologists predict a new ice age.

1957: US oceanographer Roger Revelle warns that people are conducting a 'large-scale geophysical experiment' on the planet by releasing greenhouse gases. Colleague David Keeling sets up first continuous monitoring of CO_2 levels in the atmosphere. Immediately Keeling finds regular year-on-year rise.

1970s: Series of studies by the US Department of Energy increases concerns about future global warming.

1979: First World Climate Conference adopts climate change as major issue and calls on governments 'to foresee and prevent potential man-made changes in climate'.

1985: First major international conference on the greenhouse effect at Villach, Austria, warns that greenhouse gases will 'in the first half of the next century, cause a rise of global mean temperature which is greater than any in man's history'. This could cause sea levels to rise by up to a metre, researchers say. Conference also reports that gases other than CO_2, such as methane, ozone, CFCs and nitrous oxide, will also contribute to warming.

1987: Warmest year on record. The 1980s turn out to be the warmest decade, with seven of the eight warmest years recorded up to 1990. Even the coldest years in the 1980s were warmer than the warmest years of the 1880s.

1988: Global warming attracts worldwide headlines after scientists at Congressional hearings in Washington DC blame major US drought on its influence. Meeting of climate scientists in Toronto subsequently calls for 20 per cent cuts in global CO_2 emissions by the year 2005. UN sets up the Intergovernmental Panel on Climate Change (IPCC) to analyse and report on scientific findings.

1990: The first report of the IPCC finds that the planet has warmed by 0.5°C in the past century. IPCC warns that only strong measures to halt rising greenhouse-gas emissions will prevent serious global warming. Provides scientific clout for UN negotiations for a climate convention. Negotiations begin after the UN General Assembly in December.

1991: Mount Pinatubo erupts in the Philippines, throwing debris into the stratosphere that shields the Earth from solar energy, which helps interrupt the warming trend. Average temperatures drop for two years before rising again. Scientists point out that this event shows how sensitive global temperatures are to disruption.

1992: Climate Change Convention, signed by 154 nations in Rio, agrees to prevent 'dangerous' warming from greenhouse gases and sets initial target of reducing emissions from industrialised countries to 1990 levels by the year 2000.

1994: The Alliance of Small Island States – many of whom fear they will disappear beneath the waves as sea levels rise – adopt demand for 20 per cent cuts in emissions by the year 2005. This, they say, will cap sea-level rise at 20 centimetres.

1995: Hottest year yet. In March, the Berlin Mandate is agreed by signatories at the first full meeting of the Climate Change Convention in Berlin. Industrialised nations agree on the need to negotiate real cuts in their emissions, to be concluded by the end of 1997.

In November, the IPCC casts caution to the winds and agrees that current warming 'is unlikely to be entirely natural in origin' and that 'the balance of evidence suggests a discernible human influence on global climate'. Report predicts that, under a 'business as usual' scenario, global warming by the year 2100 will be between 1°C and 3.5°C.

1996: At the second meeting of the Climate Change Convention, the US agrees for the first time to legally binding emissions targets and sides with the IPCC against influential 'sceptical' scientists. After a four-year pause, global emissions of CO_2 resume steep climb, and scientists warn that most industrialised countries will not meet Rio agreement to stabilise emissions at 1990 levels by the year 2000.

1997: Kyoto Protocol agrees legally binding emissions cuts for industrialised nations, averaging 5.4 per cent, to be met by 2010. The meeting also adopts a series of flexibility measures, allowing countries to meet their targets partly by trading emissions permits, establishing carbon sinks such as forests to soak up emissions, and by investing in other countries. The precise rules are left for further negotiations. Meanwhile, the US government says it will not ratify the agreement unless it sees evidence of 'meaningful participation' in reducing emissions from developing countries.

1998: Follow-up negotiations in Buenos Aires fail to resolve disputes over the Kyoto 'rule book', but agree on a deadline for resolution by the end of 2000. 1998 is the hottest year in the hottest decade of the hottest century of the millennium.

2000: Scientist reassess likely future emissions and warn that, if things go badly, the world could warm by 6°C within a century. Series of major floods around the world reinforce fears that global warming is raising the risk of extreme weather events. But in November, crunch talks held in The Hague to finalise the 'Kyoto rule book' fail to reach agreement after EU and US fall out. Decisions postponed until at least May 2001.

Global warming: full steam ahead

The change of power in Washington doesn't bode well for the future of the planet

It seems ironic that on the day the world's scientists issue a report saying the problem is escalating, the new US president should say he is not sure whether global warming is a reality or a threat.

Man is having a serious effect on the climate, and temperature and sea-level rises are going to be higher than was predicted in the last report five years ago, according to the latest research.

The ponderously named Intergovernmental Panel on Climate Change is a collection of 3,000 of the world's best climate scientists who have studied every aspect of climate change and come to the conclusion that it is speeding up dramatically.

In the worst case, temperatures could rise 6°C in the next century and sea levels by a metre. Add to that the regional differences – for example it gets much warmer in big landmasses like Europe and North America – and the changes are too fast for natural vegetation like trees to adapt. The result is potentially disastrous.

By Paul Brown
Environment Correspondent

One of the ironies is that some of the best and most influential scientists who have come to these conclusions are American, yet they have a Texan oil man, President George W. Bush, who is not convinced of their arguments.

Since the US emits 24% of the world's main greenhouse gas, carbon dioxide, an agreement to cut the world's emissions must include

---

Man is having a serious effect on the climate, and temperature and sea level rises are going to be higher than was predicted in the last report five years ago

---

America. When the climate talks collapsed in December, the US was blamed for refusing to make enough effort to cut its domestic emissions.

America wanted to rely on planting forests and changing agricultural practices to claim credit for emitting less carbon dioxide than it would have done otherwise. The EU rejected this as cheating.

Talks are due to resume in May 2001, but already the US has asked for a postponement until July. The reasoning is that the new administration's team – which is not yet assembled – will need until then to brief itself on the complex issues involved.

US allies, which in this case include Russia, Japan, Canada, Ukraine and Australia, are backing this stance, and, despite the irritation of Europe and developing countries such as India and China, look likely to succeed.

So while the science moves on, the political progress is stalled. Currently, the world looks as if it is racing towards climate disaster.

Climate change

Information from Greenpeace

'... we have an authoritative early warning system: an agreed assessment of some 300 of the world's leading scientists of what is happening to the world's climate... a report of historic significance... what it predicts will affect our daily lives.'

Margaret Thatcher,
15 May 1990.

Carbon dioxide and other gases in the atmosphere act like the glass in a greenhouse, trapping the heat from the sun. This is known as the 'greenhouse effect'. As more 'greenhouse gases', including CO_2, are added to the atmosphere, more heat is trapped and the world's climate grows warmer: 'climate change' occurs.

Since 1860, when records began, the world's temperature has risen by around 0.5°C. There is strong evidence that this is as a result of human-caused climate change. The amount of CO_2 in the atmosphere has risen by about 25% since the Industrial Revolution. In 1700 the atmosphere contained around 280 parts per million (ppm); today it contains around 350ppm. It is expected to contain over 450ppm of CO_2 by 2030 if we carry on as usual.

Most fossil fuel burning goes on in the industrialised world; North America, Europe, the former USSR and Japan used around three-quarters of the world's total energy in 1990. The average North American uses about six times as much energy to live as the average Latin American.

The world's 300 top climate scientists produced their first combined call for action on climate change in 1990. The Inter-governmental Panel on Climate Change (IPCC) tried to work out, on average, how much the Earth's climate is likely to heat up by the end of the 21st century and agreed a 'best estimate' of 2.5°C. Although this sounds small, a 2.5°C rise in 100 years is a much faster increase than has ever been experienced before in human history. After the last ice age, the world is thought to have warmed up, on average, by 1°C every 500 years.

Governments responded by signing the Climate Convention, agreeing to stabilise their emissions of CO_2 by 2000. However, this is a weak target: what is needed is a cut of 60-80%.

Climate change on the scale and at the speed predicted would present enormous threats to the world's species. Climate scientists believe it will lead to the following impacts:

Sea-level rise

Half of humanity lives in coastal zones. Bangladesh, the Netherlands and the small, low-lying islands of the Pacific are particularly at risk of flooding from sea-level rise, which would force their inhabitants to flee, becoming environmental refugees.

In 1996, the Carteret Islands, part of the Solomon Islands north-east of Australia, were washed over by a tidal wave. The 1,700 islanders lost their entire vegetable crop. Sea level has risen 30cm per year since 1991 in the Carterets, and it is predicted that the islands will be uninhabitable by 2001.

Severe droughts and water shortages

'The next war in the Middle East will be fought over water, not politics.'

Boutros Boutros-Ghali, UN Secretary General, 1993.

Increased temperatures will mean more of the water which falls to Earth will evaporate. Some parts of the world may have less rainfall – severe droughts may result, as well as crop failures. Conflicts may arise between nations which share water supplies.

Weather disasters

Far from a gradual, pleasant warming, climate change is expected to bring 'extreme' weather events: more intense and frequent hurricanes, storms and cyclones.

Already the insurance industry is suffering from huge claims because of storm damage.

Severe gales which swept western Europe in January 1994 brought record losses of over £2 billion. Hurricane Andrew devastated the Caribbean and south-east coast of the USA in August 1992, killing 23 people and leaving 250,000 homeless. The most expensive US disaster ever, it caused $30 billion damage.

Other expected impacts of climate change are: the spread of diseases such as malaria, which could come to Britain; explosions in populations of pests such as crop-destroying aphids; more bush and forest fires; melting glaciers and bleaching of the world's coral reefs.

• The above information is an extract from a publication called *Atmosphere Under Threat* which is produced by Greenpeace. See page 41 for their address details.

© *Greenpeace*

Global warming

Information from the Young People's Trust for the Environment

Introduction

Global warming is the increase of average world temperatures as a result of what is known as the greenhouse effect. Certain gases in the atmosphere act like glass in a greenhouse, allowing sunlight through to heat the Earth's surface but trapping the heat as it radiates back into space. As the greenhouse gases build up in the atmosphere the Earth gets hotter.

Causes

One of the main greenhouse gases is carbon dioxide (CO_2). As trees grow they take in CO_2 from the air. When the wood dies the CO_2 is returned to the air. Forest clearance and wood burning (such as happens in tropical rain forests) is increasing the latter half of the process, adding to the CO_2 in the atmosphere. Deforestation is now out of control. For example in 1987 an area of the Amazon rain forest the size of Britain was burned, adding 500 million tonnes of CO_2 to the atmosphere. The loss of the forests also means that there are fewer trees to absorb CO_2.

The recent fires in Indonesia, with more than a million hectares of forest ablaze, thanks to fires set deliberately by logging companies, are likely to have an effect on global climate, but the more immediate effect has been the cloud of smog which enveloped much of south-east Asia during September and early October 1997.

However, as large a contribution as deforestation makes, it causes less than half the yearly total of CO_2, the rest comes from the burning of coal, oil and other fossil fuels. These fossil fuels are burned in cars, power stations and factories of the wealthier nations such as the USA, Western Europe and the USSR.

Televisions, lights and computers use electricity that is created mainly from burning coal. Every time we switch on a light we are adding to the greenhouse effect. Cars are also major sources of CO_2. The average European is responsible for nearly 2.5 times as much atmospheric carbon as a Latin American. The concentration of CO_2 has increased 25% since the industrial revolution, half of this rise has been in the last 30 years. It is expected to double within decades.

Other greenhouse gases

CO_2 contributes about 50% to the greenhouse effect. The other greenhouse gases are methane, chlorofluorocarbons (CFCs) and nitrous oxide (N_2O).

Methane – is released during coal-mining activities, oil exploration and when vegetation is burnt during land clearance. The main source of methane though is agricultural activity. It is released from wetlands such as rice paddies and from animals, particularly cud-chewing species like cows. The problem with methane is that as the world population increases, agricultural activity must increase and so emissions of methane will also increase. Since the 1960s the amount of methane in the air has increased by 1% per year – twice as fast as the build-up of CO_2.

Nitrous oxide – comes from both natural and man-made processes. Man-influenced sources, which represent about 45% of output to the atmosphere, are mainly: fossil fuel combustion, as in power stations; use

of nitrogenous fertilisers; burning rain forests and human and animal waste. N_2O contributes about 6% to the greenhouse effect at the moment.

CFCs – found in fridges, air conditioners, aerosols etc. – are extremely effective greenhouse gases. Although there are lower concentrations of CFCs in the atmosphere than CO_2 they trap more heat. A CFC molecule is 10,000 times more effective in trapping heat than a CO_2 molecule, methane is about 30 times more effective. Methane molecules survive for 10 years in the atmosphere and CFCs for 110 years. It is this that causes people to want to ban them completely.

Feedback processes

CO_2 – about half the CO_2 released by burning fossil fuels is absorbed by the oceans. It is taken up by minute sea creatures or dragged to the ocean depths by the circulation of water. Recent research suggests that as the Earth heats up, the oceans will be less efficient in absorbing CO_2, leaving more in the atmosphere and so adding further to global warming.

Methane – as global temperatures become greater, so large quantities of methane stored in the frozen tundra of the north may be released. Also methane trapped in the sea bed may be freed by temperature rises.

As the world warms it causes feedback processes. Increases in temperature cause the liberation of CO_2 and methane which then cause further warming. Another feedback mechanism arises through higher air temperatures evaporating more water and so providing more cloud which both traps heat from below and reflects back sunlight from above. As the world warms, the effect of clouds could become more and more significant.

Effects

If no action is taken the greenhouse effect could lead to a rise in average global temperatures of between 1.5-4.5 degrees °C as early as the year 2030. These rises will be greater towards the poles and less at the tropics. There will also be more warming in winter than summer. Such increases will make the world hotter than it has been for more than 100,000 years. The rise will also be faster than ever before; a rise of 3 degrees °C after the last ice age took thousands of years. By the end of next century temperatures could have reached those of the time of the dinosaurs and it is doubtful if humans could survive. The effects are already showing – the ten hottest years since the 1860s have been in the last 15 years.

Storms – storms and hurricanes will become more frequent and stronger as oceans heat up causing more water to evaporate. Evidence is building up at an alarming rate. In September 1991 Japan was hit by Typhoon Mireille, its worst for 30 years. Then in September 1993 it was hit by Typhoon Yancy – the 13th that year, and the worst for 50 years. In January 1993 barometric pressure around Shetland dropped to its lowest recorded level, 915 millibars. The oil tanker *Braer* broke up in the resulting storm. In March 1993 the 'Storm of the Century' hit America, causing $1.6 billion in damage from Canada to Cuba. In December 1993 hurricane-force storms caused Britain its worst flooding for 40 years.

Droughts – continental heartlands will dry out more in summer. In 1988 the US suffered its worst heatwave and drought for 50 years. It cannot be proved that this was due to the greenhouse effect but it does give us some idea of what to expect in the future.

Floods – sea levels are already rising at a rate of 1 to 2mm each year due to expansion of the top layer of the oceans as they warm and the melting of the polar ice caps. The predicted rise by 2050 is between 20 and 50cm. This will cause increased flooding in coastal areas and river estuaries such as Bangladesh and the Nile Delta. London and many other British coastal cities will be threatened also.

It is now a priority to strengthen Britain's sea defences.

What can be done?

It is important to slow the warming as much as possible. This means using less fossil fuel, eliminating CFCs altogether, and slowing down deforestation.

This can be achieved best through energy conservation, including better use of public transport and cleaner, more efficient cars; and energy efficiency by greater use of gas which produces less CO_2 than coal and oil, and through renewable energy such as solar power. We need to stop destroying rain forests (deforestation) and start replanting trees (afforestation) to soak up carbon dioxide.

A United Nations panel has estimated that we need to reduce global fuel use by 60% immediately in order to stabilise the climate. Current commitments by those governments participating in CO_2 reduction will only lower global CO_2 by 4-6%. Although the developed industrialised nations still produce most CO_2, the rapidly developing nations of South America and Asia are increasing their CO_2 production at a much higher rate, and by 2010 they will overtake the West as the main producers of CO_2.

The developing countries are reluctant to participate in any CO_2 emission reduction plans, arguing that they did not create global warming and that it is the responsibility of developed countries to cut their own emissions or to support developing countries with financial aid. Oil-producing countries – including a significant lobby in the US – are also reluctant to have their sales reduced and have protested against action on climate change.

Nuclear power – does not produce CO_2 so could replace other forms of energy. It is necessary though, to find an effective means of safely disposing of the radioactive waste that can remain dangerous for hundreds to thousands of years.

Alternative energy – more funding is required for research and development of alternative pollution-free energy sources such as solar, wave and wind energy.

How can you help?

Ignorance – is a root cause that you can help end by telling your friends and family about the problems.

Energy – encourage people to use less electricity by insulating lofts and windows for example.

Trees – recycle paper, plant trees, avoid tropical hardwoods that don't have a 'good wood seal'.

Transport – ask your family to avoid using private transport through car sharing, public transport and by using a bicycle for shorter trips.

CFCs – we can all help by using CFC-free aerosols.

Perhaps the following statements may help to inspire you...
'Nobody made a greater mistake than he who did nothing because he could do only a little.'

(Edmund Burke)

'It is time that we realised that we all share a common future.'
(Gro Harlem Brundtland, Prime Minister of Norway, 1988)

• The above information is from the Young People's Trust for the Environment (YPTENC), 8 Leapale Road, Guildford, Surrey, GU1 4JX. Tel: 01483 539600. E-mail: info@yptenc.org.uk Web site: www.yptenc.org.uk
© *Young People's Trust for the Environment (YPTENC)*

A world of extremes as the planet hots up

Scientists predict milder winters in Britain and an end to Europe's ski industry

I f the predictions in yesterday's report by leading climate scientists proved correct, millions living in Britain and other northern climes would gain from milder winters and a longer growing season but, further south, people would suffer the consequences of intense heatwaves that would kill many unused to extreme temperatures.

Insect pests would proliferate and there would be an increase in malaria; sun-seekers would find the Mediterranean too hot for holidays in July and August.

As the intergovernmental panel on climate change set out yesterday, the Earth is warming faster than at any time in the last 10,000 years and man is causing the increase by burning fossil fuels, cutting down forests and making changes in agriculture.

The changes predicted would cause coastal areas to be inundated and lead to major population changes. They would end the ski industry in Europe, cause the disappearance of many of the world's glaciers on which communities rely for regular summer water supplies, and have serious effects on agriculture.

The growing season for many of the staple crops in Africa would be cut too short for a reliable harvest because of excess heat and lack of moisture, and in Europe the Mediterranean fringe would be too dry for cereal crops. Many of the world's forests would die because of changes in water supply and the increasing heat.

Night-time average temperatures would increasingly leave much larger areas frost-free, leading to increases in insect life. Heatwaves would increase over all northern land areas and droughts, already observed to be increasing in Africa and Asia, would become more severe.

By Paul Brown, Environment Correspondent

According to the report, nearly all land areas, including northern Europe, Asia and the United States, will warm far faster than average, possibly by as much as 8°C.

Climate models worked out by giant super-computers have become far more reliable since the last report in 1995. This, combined with the climate changes observed over two decades, has convinced scientists that something very serious is happening and that it cannot be a natural process. There is far greater unanimity among the world's scientists over the issue than among politicians.

The floods in Britain and other parts of northern Europe are entirely consistent with climate-change predictions. There has been an increase of 2% in cloud cover but it is the rise in rainfall during heavier storms that has caused the floods. This is expected to get worse each decade.

A reduction in snow cover and in the area of sea ice in the Arctic has been seen since the late 60s and is expected to accelerate. In the same period the remaining ice in the Arctic ice cap has become 40% less thick.

A fall of two weeks in the annual duration of lake and river ice-cover in mid and high latitudes of the northern hemisphere has already been observed.

A widespread retreat of mountain glaciers is expected to continue. Most of the sea-level rise observed in the last century has been caused by the melting of glaciers in places such as the Alps and because of the thermal expansion of the oceans. So far the giant ice caps on Greenland and Antarctica have been slow to react, but this will change.

Although the amount of sea-level rise in this century is slightly less than predicted in 1992, the report emphasises that the process will go on for thousands of years because of

Global surface temparatures

Global surface temperatures, relative to average for 1961-90. The top ten warmest years since the start of the instrumental record in 1860 have all occured since 1980, and of these seven, including the warmest four, have been in the 1990s. We have to be careful of over-interpreting this statistic alone, as decadal variability in climate means that warm years will tend to be found in bunches.

Source: Hadley Centre for Climate Prediction and Research, Met Office, Crown Copyright

the time taken for the giant ice sheets of Greenland and Antarctica to react to increased temperatures.

Capitals drowned

Local warming over Greenland is likely to be one to three times the global average. If this warming were sustained, the complete melting of the Greenland ice cap would result in a rise in sea level of about seven metres (23ft), enough to drown all the major capitals of the world. A local warming of 5.5°C would be likely to result in a contribution from Greenland of three metres to sea-level rise over 1,000 years.

If the West Antarctic ice sheet melted over the same period this would add another three metres to sea level.

One of the fears of scientists was that the flow of fresh water from the melting Greenland ice-cap would slow down or even halt the Gulf Stream, which warms Britain and the rest of Europe. The report says that while this may happen in the distant future, it is unlikely to have a serious effect this century.

The report says that the burning of fossil fuels is going to be 'the dominant influence' on climate in

The rate of warming is much higher than in the 20th century and at any time in the last 10,000 years since the ice age ended

the next century. As the carbon dioxide in the atmosphere increases, the ability of plant life on land and in the oceans to soak it up decreases. In 1750 the concentrations of carbon dioxide in the atmosphere were 280 ppm (parts per million). By 2000 the figure had increased 31%.

The report says the present carbon dioxide concentration has not been exceeded in the last 420,000 years and probably not for 20m years. It is now going up at the rate of 4% a decade and is expected to accelerate to reach 540ppm-970ppm by the end of the century. If it reaches the top of this range the temperature will rise up to 6°C, two degrees higher than predicted five years ago.

The rate of warming is much higher than in the 20th century and at any time in the last 10,000 years since the ice age ended.

Methane concentrations have gone up 151% since 1750, partly due to fossil fuel burning, but also because of increase in rice culture and cattle, both of which generate methane from rotting vegetation. Landfill sites produce methane for the same reason but there are signs that these increases are levelling off.

Nitrous oxide, also a potent greenhouse gas, produced by industry, motor transport and agriculture, continues to increase and concentrations have not been exceeded in 1,000 years.

Other attempts by man to reduce pollution for other reasons are now known to increase global warming. The complex atmospheric changes which cause the hole in the ozone layer also allow heat to escape from the Earth. If the ozone hole is mended, as scientists predict it will be, then the Earth will heat up faster than it otherwise would.

Stopping acid rain and reducing the burning of forests will also allow more heat to reach the Earth. This will partly be offset by an increase in tiny droplets of water from storms and spray but the net effect will be a warmer Earth.

The ozone layer

Information from the Young People's Trust for the Environment

What is the ozone layer?

Ozone is a naturally occurring gas found in the atmosphere where it absorbs most of the sun's ultraviolet light – invisible rays which are harmful to both plant and animal life.

Ozone is found throughout the atmosphere including ground level, but is mostly found in a band called the ozone layer at about 15-40km above the Earth's surface. The ozone layer is essential for life – until it was formed, about a billion years ago, the only life on Earth was at the bottom of the ocean.

At lower levels in the atmosphere ozone acts as a greenhouse gas helping trap heat and so contributes to global warming.

Destruction of the ozone layer – the causes

Chlorofluorocarbons (CFCs) have been identified as the cause of the destruction to the ozone layer. They are found in refrigerators, air conditioning packaging and propellants. They were discovered by Thomas Midgeley in 1930 as a cheap, safe coolant for refrigerators. CFCs are very stable, they decay slowly and so endure in the atmosphere for up to a century.

CFCs rise and gradually accumulate in the stratosphere where they are broken down by the sun's ultraviolet light, so releasing chlorine atoms. The chlorine attacks the ozone, one chlorine atom can help to destroy 100,000 ozone molecules.

The effects

With the chlorine from CFCs destroying the ozone, more ultraviolet light is able to reach the Earth's surface, with harmful effect to human and plant life. The harmful radiation is known as UV-B.

UV-B radiation can cause skin cancer, cataracts and increased infections through the skin. It has an adverse effect on plants. There is also a threat to phyto-plankton, the single-cell plants that all marine life depends on, as it is highly sensitive to UV-B radiation. This could upset the ocean food chain on which we depend for fish and also much of our oxygen.

Skin cancer is the most obvious problem as it is estimated that a 10%

loss of ozone above Britain could cause an extra 8,000 cases of skin cancer every year.

The Antarctic ozone hole

A hole in the ozone layer, covering an area larger than the Antarctic continent, was discovered in 1985 by Joe Farman and his colleagues on the British Antarctic Survey. They discovered a general thinning over the whole globe – a 3% decrease since 1969, but with greater depletions in middle and higher northern latitudes in winter. Every winter the ozone layer thins by up to 8% over Europe.

Although there is no hole over the Arctic, experts have found that concentrations of chlorine are 50 times greater than expected.

In 1979 the USA and Scandinavia banned CFCs in aerosols. In 1985 the United Nations Convention on Protection of the Ozone Layer was drawn up. This was the first practical step towards limiting CFCs.

On 1st January 1989 the Montreal Protocol came into force. It is the actual agreement to reduce consumption of CFCs. Thirty-three nations and the European Community have signed, committing them to cut CFC production by half before the end of the century. From 1st January 2000 CFCs will be banned from all new refrigerators and freezers. However the developing countries, such as India and China, will be allowed to continue using CFCs until the year 2010.

Green consumerism can contribute towards saving the ozone layer. CFC-free aerosol cans and plastic foam containers are now available to buyers. The Environmental Health Officer can now arrange to take away old fridges so that the CFCs can be recovered and recycled. Some manufacturers now offer fridges with the CFCs in the insulation panels cut by at least 50%.

It is necessary to achieve the global phase-out of CFCs very quickly. The US Environmental Protection Agency reported that, even if all countries phased out CFCs by 1990, it would take until 2050 for the level of chlorine in the stratosphere to return to 1985 levels. This is because CFCs decompose so slowly.

• The above information is from the Young People's Trust for the Environment, 8 Leapale Road, Guildford, Surrey, GU1 4JX. Tel: 01483 539600. E-mail: info@yptenc.org.uk Web site: www.yptenc.org.uk

The impact of climate change on the UK

Information from Friends of the Earth

Better weather?

Models predict more winter rainfall for the whole of the UK, but especially for the south (up to 10% more by 2050).

In the summer, there should be less rain in the south in the summer but more in the north.

Both drought in the south-east and flooding in the north-west might become more common.

By 2020, it should on average be 1°C warmer than during the period 1961-1990, which is equivalent to a 200 km northward shift in climate.[1]

Climate change might affect the gulf stream, so there is a possibility that it might get colder rather than warmer.

Unpleasant surprises

Blood-sucking ticks are on the increase. Ticks are favoured by climate change as they like mild winters and warm summers. They can harbour unusual fatal diseases, such as Crimean Congo Haemorrhagic Fever, which are expected to reach the UK soon.[2]

Higher temperatures will increase peat decomposition, resulting in a massive run-off into water systems. This would mean discoloured water, with the annual clean-up bill to reach millions in northern England and Scotland.

Algal blooms on rivers and lakes are expected to increase.

Warm weather also favours various house pests such as cockroaches, fleas and mites.

Water shortages

Higher temperatures result in more evaporation, so more water will be lost from resevoirs.

Warmer weather will mean increases in public and agricultural demand for water, especially for gardens and spray irrigation. Between 1991 and 2021, water demand in the south and the east is expected to more than double, with 46% of the increase due to climate change.[3]

Water companies are already arguing for the building of more reservoirs, which will destroy valuable habitats. Sorting out the enormous leakages (up to 38%) from the water supply system, as well as demand side management, is thus ever more crucial.

Ecosystems in danger

Wetlands would be adversely affected by droughts, threatening many bird species.

Erosion of coastal habitats is already happening in East Anglia and reducing the number of breeding birds.

10% of nature reserves in the UK (National Nature Reserves and Sites of Special Scientific Interest) occur near sea level on the coast. Especially mudflats and salt marshes, both of which are important bird habitats, are threatened. E.g. 60% of the UK redshank population nests in salt marshes.[1]

Heather moorland would disappear in favour of bracken, with adverse effects on merlin, golden plover, red grouse and curlew.[4]

Your health

Warmer temperatures would enable insects and other disease carriers to expand their range.

Malaria-carrying mosquitoes are unlikely to reach the UK but may well affect some of our most popular tourist destinations in southern Spain and Italy.

Urban air pollution will be aggravated by higher temperatures, which will be particularly serious for asthma sufferers.

Money matters

In the UK, the summer of 1995 was the warmest and driest on record. Furthermore, the 12-month period from November 1994 to October 1995 was the warmest on record. The experience of this period gives a first indication of what a warmer climate might mean for the UK, as elaborated by a recent report commissioned by the Department of the Environment.[5]

- large losses of around £200 million in livestock farming. Lower yields for potatoes and other vegetables but gains to arable crops (£30 million)
- the prices for summer vegetables were 20 to 30% higher than normal as lack of water damaged crops
- higher water supply costs (£96 million)
- net savings in energy because of the mild winter (£355 million)

Mounting evidence? Unusual weather in the UK

Since 1988	Annual rainfall below long-term average, except in 1994
1995	0.38°C warmer than average (plus warmest year on record in UK and globally)
Oct. 1996	Strongest gales since hurricane of 1987
Dec. 1996	Half normal rainfall
1996	0.21°C warmer than average
January 1997	Driest January on record (15.8mm of rain against an average of 88mm)
March 1997	One of seven driest Marches this century (23mm of rain against normal 72mm)
April 1997	River Thames is flowing at 1/3 of its normal rate
June 1997	The wettest June since 1879, more than twice the normal rainfall (in Newcastle and East Anglia even 3 times)
1995	Average global temperature reached 15.39°C, previous high 15.38°C in 1990. The 10 warmest years in the last 130 have all occured in the 1980s and 1990s.

Of course, it could be natural variability. But it will be decades before we can say for definite that these are global, long-term trends and waiting for certainty means that we would waste valuable time instead of taking measures we should be taking anyway.

- losses in the retail sector (£87 million) – gains in beer/wine/fruit and vegetable sales, losses in clothing sales
- unusually high losses by insurance industry for subsidence-related damage, although lower pay-outs for burst pipes (net cost £175-350 million)
- net increase in road maintenance costs but these can be accomodated in future (new British Standard for asphalting)
- increase of 54% in number of fires, but no figures available on costs

On balance, negative economic effects exceeded positive ones.

The UK and global impacts

Climate change could have serious negative effects on global food production, which would have implications on food supplies and prices in the UK.

The projected increase in extreme weather events (cyclones etc.) will be very costly for the insurance industry. Damage elsewhere will affect insurance premiums in the UK because of the international nature of the insurance industry.

The negative effects of climate change in many nations can lead to political instabilities both regionally and globally.

Numbers of environmental refugees could rocket, requiring a major international aid and relocation effort.

References

1 Climate Change Impacts Review Group (1996) *Review of the Potential Effects of Climate Change in the United Kingdom*, London: HMSO.
2 *The Guardian* 10 January 1997.
3 Herrington (1996), quoted in Arnell, N. (1996) *Global Warming, River Flows and Water Resources*, Chichester: Wiley.
4 According to John Lawton, NERC & Imperial College, quoted in Nuttal, N. (1996) 'Scientists may have overplayed threat of global warming', *The Times* 25 October 1996.
5 Palutikof, J.P., Subak, S. and Agnew, M.D. (1997) *Economic Impacts of the Hot Summer and Unusually Warm Year of 1995*, Norwich: University of East Anglia.

© Friends of the Earth

Biodiversity and climate change

Information from the United Nations Environmental Programme (UNEP) and the World Conservation Monitoring Centre (WCMC)

The world's climate patterns have always been highly dynamic. Recent decades, however, have seen new patterns, indicating more rapid changes than have been seen for thousands of years.

These changes have been linked to equally rapid changes in atmospheric chemistry, and the release of 'greenhouse gases' by human activities.

For the first time in the history of our planet a single species is driving a significant shift in the global climate.

International efforts are being focused towards reducing the amounts of gas emissions, however climate changes have already begun, and the impacts will increase considerably over coming decades no matter how successful the efforts at emissions reductions.

Global biodiversity is under particular risk. Already hemmed in by habitat loss, pollution and over-exploitation, species and natural systems are now faced with the need to adapt to new regimes of temperature, precipitation and other climatic extremes. Nature conservation in the new millennium has increasingly difficult challenges to face.

The changing climate

The world's climate has always been highly variable. Many changes are driven by natural factors, but others are now the result of human activities.

Human influences on the climate

- The use of fossil fuel currently accounts for 80 to 85% of the carbon dioxide being added to the atmosphere. Carbon dioxide is an important greenhouse gas and increasing concentrations lead to a heating of the atmosphere. Concentrations have increased by 25% over the last 200 years, primarily as a result of burning coal, oil, and natural gas (e.g. in automobiles, industry, and electricity generation).
- Land use changes, e.g. clearing land for logging, ranching, and agriculture, account for a further 15 to 20% of current carbon dioxide emissions. Vegetation contains carbon that is released as carbon dioxide when the vegetation decays or burns.
- The amount of carbon dioxide in the atmosphere will double during the twenty-first century if the current trends in emissions continue, with further increases thereafter. The amounts of several other greenhouse gases will increase substantially as well.

Natural changes in climate

- Large volcanic eruptions put tiny particles in the atmosphere that block sunlight, resulting in a surface cooling of a few years' duration.
- Variations in ocean currents change the distribution of heat and precipitation. El Niño events (periodic warming of the ocean surface central and eastern tropical Pacific Ocean) typically last one to two years and change weather patterns around the world, causing heavy rains in some places and droughts in others.
- Over longer time spans, tens or hundreds of thousands of years, natural changes in the energy received from the sun, or in the balance of greenhouse gases or dust in the atmosphere have caused the climate to shift from ice ages to relatively warmer periods, such as the one we are currently experiencing.

Facts and figures

- Greenhouse gas is a term used to describe a range of gases which trap radiation emitted from Earth's surface, and hence keep the planet far warmer than it would otherwise be. Carbon dioxide, methane, nitrous oxides and ozone are all greenhouse gases. The order of importance in

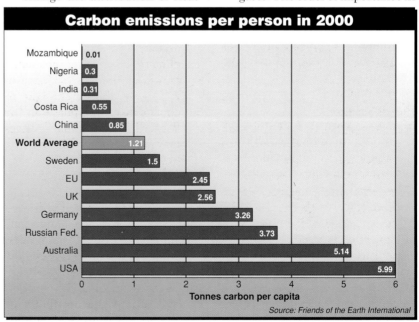

Carbon emissions per person in 2000

Country	Tonnes carbon per capita
Mozambique	0.01
Nigeria	0.3
India	0.31
Costa Rica	0.55
China	0.85
World Average	1.21
Sweden	1.5
EU	2.45
UK	2.56
Germany	3.26
Russian Fed.	3.73
Australia	5.14
USA	5.99

Source: Friends of the Earth International

contributing to human-induced global warming is carbon dioxide (70%), methane (20%) and others (10%).

- Average global surface temperatures have increased by 0.3-0.6°C since the late nineteenth century, most of this (0.2-0.3°C) has occurred in the last 40 years. Regional analysis of these statistics have shown even greater increases in some areas: Arctic regions have shown a 0.6°C rise since 1979.
- There is slightly more carbon dioxide in the northern hemisphere than in the southern hemisphere. The difference arises because most of the human activities that produce carbon dioxide are in the north and it takes about a year for northern hemispheric emissions to circulate through the atmosphere and reach southern latitudes.
- The global average sea level has risen by 10 to 25 cm over the past 100 years. It is likely that much of this rise is related to an increase of 0.3-0.6°C in the lower atmosphere's global average temperature since 1860.
- Glaciers are in retreat on every continent. This loss of ice over the past 100 years has added about 2 to 4 cm to the sea level.
- Temperature has not increased as much as expected from the observed CO_2 increase. This is related to increases in the amounts of tiny particles in the air arising, for instance, from industrial activities or volcanic eruptions. These block out some sunlight and induce a reversing cooling effect.

Future scenarios

- Increases of 1 to 3.5°C (about 2 to 6°F) in globally averaged surface temperatures have been projected by the Inter-governmental Panel on Climate Change (IPCC) by the year 2100, as compared with 1990. This projection is based on estimates of future concentrations of greenhouse gases and sulphate particles in the atmosphere. The average rate of warming of the Earth's surface over the next

hundred years will probably be greater than any that has occurred in the last 10,000 years, the period over which civilisation developed. However, specific temperature changes will vary considerably from region to region. The maximum warming is expected to occur in the Arctic in winter. Both evaporation and precipitation will increase in many regions, according to most climate change models, as will the frequency of intense rainfalls. Some regions that are already drought-prone may suffer longer and more severe dry spells. In spring, faster snow melt may aggravate flooding.

- Sea levels will rise another 15 to 95 cm by the year 2100 (with a 'best estimate' of 50 cm). This will occur from the combination of thermal expansion of ocean water with the increased influx of freshwater from melting glaciers and ice-sheets. The projected rise is two to five times faster than the rise experienced over the past 100 years.
- Extreme weather events such as tropical storms are more difficult to predict, as indeed are the more fine-scale patterns of change at local levels. This uncertainty results from the existence of large natural regional variations, as well as limitations in computer models and the understanding of the relationship between local and global climate.
- Changes may be very rapid. Most predictions are based on the assumption that the global climate will change gradually. However, there is evidence of relatively abrupt changes to climate at various phases in the Earth's history. Similar changes may well be induced again in the near future. It has been suggested, for example, that increasing temperatures may result in massive release of carbon dioxide from the soil as permafrost melts and peat deposits are broken down. This will add to climate warming and further accelerate permafrost melting. Other models have raised the possibility of abrupt changes in ocean currents.

Impacts on biodiversity

Climate change is likely to have considerable impacts on most or all ecosystems. The distribution patterns of many species and communities are determined to a large part by climatic parameters, however, the responses to changes in these parameters are rarely simple.

Shifts in distribution of plants and animals

At the simplest level, changing patterns of climate will change the natural distribution limits for species or communities. In the absence of barriers it may be possible for species or communities to migrate in response to changing conditions. Vegetation zones may move towards higher latitudes or higher altitudes following shifts in average temperatures. Movements will be more pronounced at higher latitudes where temperatures are expected to rise more than near the equator. In the mid-latitude regions (45 to 60°), for example, present temperature zones could shift by 150 – 550 km.

Barriers to movement

In most cases natural or man-made barriers will impact the natural movement of species or communities. Arctic tundra and alpine meadows may become squeezed by the natural configuration of the landscape, while these and many other natural systems may be further confined by human land-use patterns. Many national parks and protected areas are now surrounded by urban and agricultural landscapes which will prevent the simple migration of species beyond their boundaries.

Changing patterns of precipitation and evaporation

Rainfall and drought will also be of critical importance. Extreme flooding will have implications for large areas, especially riverine and valley ecosystems. Increasing drought and desertification may occur in tropical and sub-tropical zones, and at least one model has predicted a drying out of large parts of the Amazon.

Rapid changes

Rates of change will also be important, and these will vary at regional and even local levels. The maximum rates of spread for some sedentary species, including large tree-species may, be slower than the predicted rates of change in climatic conditions.

Species interaction
In many cases further complications will arise from the complexity of species interactions and differential sensitivities to changing conditions between species. Certain species may rapidly adapt to new conditions and may act in competition with others.

Shifting seasons
Changes in seasons are already being noticed in many temperate regions. Birdsong is being reported earlier and spring flowers are emerging when it was once winter. In agricultural landscapes changes in the length of growing seasons may improve productivity in mid-latitudes and increase the potential for arable crops at high latitudes. Negative impacts

---

The world's climate has always been highly variable. Many changes are driven by natural factors, but others are now the result of human activities

---

may include increased ranges of insect pests and diseases, and failure of crops in some regions from drought or flooding.

The coastal margins
On the relatively narrow habitats of the coastal margins, especially where these are backed by areas of intense human use, rising sea levels may lead to the squeezing out of important coastal habitats.

Warmer oceans
Rising sea temperatures will further affect the distribution and survival of particular marine resources. Corals have already shown an extremely high sensitivity to minor increases in temperature, while other studies have shown dramatic changes in the distribution and survival of the Pacific salmon in the late 1990s.

Chemical effects
In addition to causing a warming effect, increased concentrations of atmospheric carbon dioxide are known to increase rates of photo-synthesis in many plants, as well as improving water use efficiency. In this way the climate changes may increase growth rates in some natural and agricultural communities.

• The above information is from the UNEP-WCMC web site which can be found at www.unep-wcmc.org/
© UNEP-WCMC

Kyoto Protocol

The background

The United Nations Framework Convention on Climate Change (UNFCCC) was signed by the overwhelming majority of world leaders at the 'Earth Summit' in Rio de Janeiro in 1992. In the UNFCCC, which came into force in 1994, contracting countries all agree (in Article Two) to 'achieve stabilisation of greenhouse gas concentrations in the atmosphere at a level that would prevent dangerous anthropogenic interference with the climate system . . . within a time frame sufficient to allow ecosystems to adapt naturally to climate change, to ensure that food production is not threatened, and to enable economic development to proceed in a sustainable manner'.

Developed nations (those of the OECD and the former Warsaw Pact) also committed to reduce their emissions of greenhouse gases in 2000 to the 1990 level.

Further targets for the control of greenhouse gases were agreed at the third conference of the parties to the convention at Kyoto, Japan, in 1997, giving rise to the Kyoto Protocol. This requires developed countries to reduce their annual emissions of greenhouse gases by (on average) 5.2 per cent from the 1990 level by 2008-2012. The EU undertook to achieve an 8 per cent reduction, within which the UK is required to cut its emissions by 12.5 per cent.

A key part of the Kyoto Protocol is that some of the emission reductions required of developed countries may be met by transferring reductions in emissions across national boundaries, under the so-called 'flexibility mechanisms' (FMs). These take three forms:

• Emissions Trading – a developed country that has exceeded its Kyoto targets to reduce carbon dioxide emissions can sell its surplus reduction to another developed country that has failed to meet its target.

• Joint Implementation – a developed country can fund a project in another developed country that will either reduce carbon dioxide emissions (such as improving the efficiency of a power station), or enhance carbon 'sinks' (such as TEPCO's carbon forestry in Tasmania). The reduction of carbon dioxide in the atmosphere is allocated to the country financing the project.

• Clean Development Mechanism – a developed country can fund a project in an undeveloped country that will either reduce carbon dioxide emissions, or enhance carbon 'sinks'. Such projects must produce 'reductions in emissions that are additional to any that would occur in the absence of the certified project activity'.

• Last month's COP6 talks in The Hague were intended to define the rules applying to the targets, in particular over the application of the 'Flexibility Mechanisms' and the use of 'sinks' (such as forests or plantations of fast-growing trees) to absorb carbon dioxide.

Wet Britain, warm world

The year 2000. Information from the Met Office

The year 2000 is set to be the wettest year across England and Wales since 1872 according to figures released by the Met Office today. Globally, the current trend of very warm years continues. The global mean surface temperature in 2000 is expected to be similar to 1999; this was the fifth warmest year since records began in 1860. According to a new forecasting technique developed at the Met Office, 2001 is expected to be warmer still.

A number of rainfall records were broken across England and Wales during the year. Notably the year saw the wettest April and wettest autumn since records began in 1766. Currently the annual rainfall total, averaged across England and Wales, is 1192 mm but it seems unlikely the total will pass the 1284 mm recorded in 1872. Central England temperature statistics also reveal another warm, but not record-breaking, year with 2000 likely to rank in the ten warmest years since records began in 1659.

The global statistics, revealed today by the World Meteorological Organisation in Geneva, are com-

piled using data analysed by the Met Office and the University of East Anglia. The global mean temperature is likely to be about 0.32°C above the 1961-90 normal. Since records began 140 years ago only 1998, 1997, 1995 and 1990 have been warmer.

David Parker of the Met Office's Hadley Centre said: 'There have now been 22 years in a row with above-average global temperatures. The ten warmest years on record since 1860 have all occurred since 1983, and eight of the top ten have occurred since 1990. When we look at patterns of change, we increasingly believe that a large part of the recent warming is due to fossil fuel burning.'

The new Met Office technique to forecast global mean temperatures a year ahead takes account of the intensity of the widely reported El Niño phenomenon in the Pacific. The technique also incorporates increasing amounts of greenhouse gases, such as carbon dioxide, in the atmosphere.

Professor Alan Thorpe, Director of the Hadley Centre, said: 'Our experimental forecast suggests that, globally speaking, 2001 may be the second warmest year on record, but the warmth will depend on whether the anticipated El Niño develops in the tropical Pacific.'

Notes
1 With 13 days remaining in 2000, all figures contained in the news release were provisional. However, the global 'ranking' relative to other years is unlikely to change.
2 The accuracy of the experimental forecast for 2001 depends on the expected development of a relatively strong El Niño during the year.
3 The period over which averages have been calculated is 1961-90.

© Crown copyright Met Office 2000

Fast facts

Global warming is sending life on Earth into a sweat!

- Emissions of carbon dioxide, the main global warming gas, are now around 12 times higher than in 1900. Most carbon dioxide (CO_2) comes from burning coal, oil and natural gas for energy.
- Western nations' CO_2 emissions are up to 25 times higher per head of population than in developing countries. No wonder concerned organisations say that industrialised countries need to set an example.
- Atmospheric levels of global warming gases are higher now than at any time in the past 420,000 years.
- The world is warming faster than at any time in the last 10,000 years, with the 1990s being the hottest decade in the past millennium.

The changes are evident from the Equator to the poles:

- Rising sea levels threaten the populations of low-lying islands in the Pacific and Indian islands.
- Cities like Chicago, Athens and New Delhi have sweltered under heat waves and seen death tolls rise.
- Coral reefs around the world have been severely damaged by unusually high ocean temperatures.
- North Pacific salmon populations crashed after ocean temperatures in the region soared 6°C (9°F) above normal.
- Food shortages linked to warming seas led to hundreds of thousands of seabird deaths off the coast of the US state of California.
- Europe's alpine glaciers have lost half their volume since 1850. The

US government predicts there will be no glaciers left in Montana's Glacier National Park by 2030.

- Dramatic reductions in Arctic ice cover.
- The rapid rate of warming puts one-third of the world's forests at risk, as well as the species that depend on forests for their survival.

• The above information is from Climate Voice's web site which can be found at www.climatevoice.org Climate Voice is a new co-operation between a wide range of organisations around the world which want to see more action taken against global warming. The site is managed by WWF International. Each organisation involved is working to prevent global warming and climate change.

© Climate Voice

Melting of earth's ice cover reaches new high

By Lisa Mastny

The Earth's ice cover is melting in more places and at higher rates than at any time since record keeping began. Reports from around the world compiled by the Worldwatch Institute show that global ice melting accelerated during the 1990s – which was also the warmest decade on record.

Scientists suspect that the enhanced melting is among the first observable signs of human-induced global warming, caused by the unprecedented release of carbon dioxide and other greenhouse gases over the past century. Glaciers and other ice features are particularly sensitive to temperature shifts.

The Earth's ice cover acts as a protective mirror, reflecting a large share of the sun's heat back into space and keeping the planet cool. Loss of the ice would not only affect the global climate, but would also raise sea levels and spark regional flooding, damaging property and endangering lives. Large-scale melting would also threaten key water supplies as well as alter the habitats of many of the world's plant and animal species.

Some of the most dramatic reports come from the polar regions, which are warming faster than the planet as a whole and have lost large amounts of ice in recent decades. The Arctic sea ice, covering an area roughly the size of the United States, shrank by an estimated 6 per cent between 1978 and 1996, losing an average of 34,300 square kilometres – an area larger than the Netherlands – each year.

The Arctic sea ice has also thinned dramatically since the 1960s and 70s. Between this period and the mid-1990s, the average thickness dropped from 3.1 meters to 1.8 metres – a decline of nearly 40 per cent in less than 30 years.

The Arctic's Greenland Ice Sheet – the largest mass of land-

Selected examples of ice melt around the world

Name	Location	Measured loss
Arctic Sea Ice	Arctic Ocean	Has shrunk by 6 per cent since 1978, with a 14 per cent loss of thicker, year-round ice. Has thinned by 40 per cent in less than 30 years.
Greenland Ice Sheet	Greenland	Has thinned by more than a metre a year on its southern and eastern edges since 1993.
Columbia Glacier	Alaska, USA	Has retreated nearly 13 kilometres since 1982. In 1999, retreat rate increased from 25 metres per day to 35 metres per day.
Glacier National Park	Rocky Mtns, USA	Since 1850, the number of glaciers has dropped from 150 to fewer than 50. Remaining glaciers could disappear completely in 30 years.
Antarctic Sea Ice	Southern Ocean	Ice to the west of the Antarctic Peninsula decreased by some 20 per cent between 1973 and 1993, and continues to decline.
Pine Island Glacier	West Antarctica	Grounding line (where glacier hits ocean and floats) retreated 1.2 kilometres a year between 1992 and 1996. Ice thinned at a rate of 3.5 metres per year.
Larsen B Ice Shelf	Antarctic Peninsula	Calved a 200km^2 iceberg in early 1998. Lost an additional 1,714km^2 during the 1998-1999 season, and 300km^2 so far during the 1999-2000 season.
Tasman Glacier	New Zealand	Terminus has retreated 3 kilometres since 1971, and main front has retreated 1.5 kilometres since 1982. Has thinned by up to 200 metres on average since the 1971-82 period. Icebergs began to break off in 1991, accelerating the collapse.
Duosuogang Peak	Ulan Ula Mtns, China	Glaciers have shrunk by some 60 per cent since the early 1970s.
Tien Shan Mtns.	Central Asia	Twenty-two per cent of glacial ice volume has disappeared in the past 40 years.
Caucasus Mtns.	Russia	Glacial volume has declined by 50 per cent in the past century.
Alps	Western Europe	Glacial area has shrunk by 35 to 40 per cent and volume has declined by more than 50 per cent since 1850. Glaciers could be reduced to only a small fraction of their present mass within decades.
Speka Glacier	Uganda	Retreated by more than 150 metres between 1977 and 1990, compared with only 35-45 metres between 1958 and 1977.

Source: Worldwatch Institute

based ice outside of Antarctica, with 8 per cent of the world's ice – has thinned more than a metre per year on average since 1993 along parts of its southern and eastern edges.

The massive Antarctic ice cover, which averages 2.3 kilometres in thickness and represents some 91 per cent of Earth's ice, is also melting. So far, most of the loss has occurred along the edges of the Antarctic Peninsula, on the ice shelves that form when the land-based ice sheets flow into the ocean and begin to float. Within the past decade, three ice shelves have fully disintegrated: the Wordie, the Larsen A, and the Prince Gustav. Two more, the Larsen B and the Wilkins, are in full retreat and are expected to break up soon, having lost more than one-seventh of their combined 21,000 square kilometres since late 1998 – a loss the size of Rhode Island. Icebergs as big as Delaware have also broken off Antarctica in recent years, posing threats to open-water shipping.

Antarctica's vast land ice is also melting, although there is disagreement over how quickly. One study estimates that the Western Antarctic Ice Sheet (WAIS), the smaller of the continent's two ice sheets, has retreated at an average rate of 122 metres a year for the past 7,500 years- and is in no imminent danger of collapse. But other studies suggest that the sheet may break more abruptly if melting accelerates. They point to signs of past collapse, as well as to fast-moving ice streams within the sheet that could speed ice melt, as evidence of potential instability.

Outside the poles, most ice melt has occurred in mountain and subpolar glaciers, which have responded much more rapidly to temperature changes. As a whole, the world's glaciers are now shrinking faster than they are growing, and losses in 1997-98 were 'extreme,' according to the World Glacier Monitoring Service. Scientists predict that up to a quarter of global mountain glacier mass could disappear by 2050, and up to one-half by 2100 – leaving large patches only in Alaska, Patagonia, and the Himalayas. Within the next 35 years, the Himalayan glacial area alone is expected to shrink by one-fifth, to 100,000 square kilometres.

The disappearance of Earth's ice cover would significantly alter the global climate – though the net effects remain unknown. Ice, particularly polar ice, reflects large amounts of solar energy back into space, and helps keep the planet cool. When ice melts, however, this exposes land and water surfaces that retain heat – leading to even more melt and creating a feedback loop that accelerates the overall warming process. But excessive ice melt in the Arctic could also have a cooling effect in parts of Europe and the eastern United States, as the influx of fresh water into the North Atlantic may disrupt ocean circulation patterns that enable the warm Gulf Stream to flow north.

As mountain glaciers shrink, large regions that rely on glacial runoff for water supply could experience severe shortages. The Quelccaya Ice Cap, the traditional water source for Lima, Peru, is now retreating by some 30 metres a year – up from only 3 metres a year before 1990 – posing a threat to the city's 10 million residents. And in northern India, a region already facing severe water scarcity, an estimated 500 million people depend on the tributaries of the glacier-fed Indus and Ganges

Research should not be dismissed by sceptics

By Philip Eden

A recent report in *Geophysical Research Letters* adds to our knowledge of how the global climate machine works, and at the same time it emphasises that there are still large areas where that knowledge is limited or non-existent.

The work was conducted by academic and government scientists who are often accused by climate-change sceptics of talking up global warming to gain more public funding for their research. If this new information is seized upon by sceptics as evidence that changes in the global climate are less dramatic than some have thought, they must also acknowledge the importance of continuing research.

Nor should anyone run away with the idea that this information disproves that there is a warming trend in the Earth's climate at the moment. However, those who seek to blame recent bad weather on global climate change are certainly barking up the wrong tree.

I would far rather listen to research scientists like these who keep their heads down and publish their work in learned journals, than to those employed by environmental pressure groups or by big American corporations who make a lot of noise but actually know very little.

© *Telegraph Group Limited, London 2001*

rivers for irrigation and drinking water. But as the Himalayas melt, these rivers are expected to initially swell and then fall to dangerously low levels, particularly in summer. (In 1999, the Indus reached record high levels because of glacial melt.)

Rapid glacial melting can also cause serious flood damage, particularly in heavily populated regions such as the Himalayas. In Nepal, a glacial lake burst in 1985, sending a 15-metre wall of water rushing 90 kilometres down the mountains, drowning people and destroying houses. A second lake near the country's Imja Glacier has now grown to 50 hectares, and is predicted to burst within the next five years, with similar consequences.

Large-scale ice melt would also raise sea levels and flood coastal areas, currently home to about half the

world's people. Over the past century, melting in ice caps and mountain glaciers has contributed on average about one-fifth of the estimated 10-25 centimetre (4-10 inch) global sea-level rise – with the rest caused by thermal expansion of the ocean as the Earth warmed. But ice melt's share in sea-level rise is increasing, and will accelerate if the larger ice sheets crumble. Antarctica alone is home to 70 per cent of the planet's fresh water, and collapse of the WAIS, an ice mass the size of Mexico,

would raise sea levels by an estimated 6 metres – while melting of both Antarctic ice sheets would raise them nearly 70 metres. (Loss of the Arctic sea ice or of the floating Antarctic ice shelves would have no effect on sea level because these already displace water.)

Wildlife is already suffering as a result of global ice melt – particularly at the poles, where marine mammals, seabirds, and other creatures depend on food found at the ice edge. In northern Canada, reports of hunger and weight loss among polar bears have been correlated with changes in the ice cover. And in Antarctica, loss of the sea ice, together with rising air temperatures and increased precipitation, is altering the habitats as well as feeding and breeding patterns of penguins and seals.

© *Worldwatch Institute*

Climate change

An update of recent research from the Hadley Centre

- Global average temperature in 1999 was lower than in the record-breaking year of 1998, but 1999 was still the fifth warmest year since global records began in 1860.
- Over the last 100 years, warming has been accompanied by a reduction in the frequency of frosts, and an increase in the number of heatwaves, in many parts of the world. The number of days of heavy rain is increasing in some countries.
- Comparison of the observed patterns of warming with model-simulated patterns of warming resulting from natural and man-made factors, indicates that over the last 50 years most of the observed change can be explained by human activities, mainly production of CO_2 from burning fossil fuels.
- Based on the recent IPCC scenarios of future emissions, the Hadley Centre predicts a global warming over the next 100 years of between 2°C and 4°C. Warming over land is expected to be some 80% faster than over sea; the

highest emission scenario would lead to an almost 6°C rise over land by 2100.
- Uncertainties in estimates of temperature rise remain high, but poorly quantified. The use of hundreds of different, but plausible, climate models will enable a proper statistical estimate of uncertainty to be built up, which (unlike the current IPCC 1.5°C to 4.5°C) can be used in risk assessments.
- Climate change will disrupt the large natural cycle of carbon dioxide between atmosphere, ocean and land. This is the first time that we have included this interaction in a climate model, and find that CO_2 in the atmosphere rises much faster, leading to approximately 40% greater warming. Although the results are not definitive, they do show the potential of this feedback to accelerate warming. The temperature increases given above do not include this effect.
- Planting trees ('Kyoto forests') will absorb CO_2 from the atmo-

sphere. However, in some parts of the world, climate change may lead to less rapid tree growth, or even die back, and hence less uptake of CO_2, than envisaged.
- Because trees are usually darker than the underlying surface (especially snow), they will absorb more sunlight than areas with no trees and hence act to warm the planet. Therefore the beneficial effects on climate of their carbon uptake could be reduced (and, in some areas, reversed) by their darkening effect.
- Although subject to the same gross uncertainties as global climate models, regional climate models provide better detail by taking account of mountains and coasts which are poorly represented in the global model. The Hadley Centre plans to develop a regional climate model that could be run for any area of the world on a PC, as input to vulnerability and adaptation assessments.

© *Crown copyright Met Office 2000*

Global warming claims 'based on false data'

By Robert Matthews

Fresh doubt has been cast on evidence for global warming following the discovery that a key method of measuring temperature change has exaggerated the warming rate by almost 40 per cent.

Studies of temperature records dating back more than a century have seemed to indicate a rise in global temperature of around 0.5°C, with much of it occurring since the late 1970s. This has led many scientists to believe that global warming is under way, with the finger of blame usually pointed at man-made pollution such as carbon dioxide.

Now an international team of scientists, including researchers from the Met Office in Bracknell, Berkshire, has found serious discrepancies in these temperature measurements, suggesting that the amount of global warming is much less than previously believed.

The concern focuses on the temperature of the atmosphere over the sea, which covers almost three-quarters of the Earth's surface. While scientists use standard weather station instruments to detect warming on land, they have been forced to rely on the crews of ships to make measurements over the vast ocean regions.

Crews have taken the temperature by dipping buckets into the sea or using water flowing into the engine intakes. Scientists have assumed that there is a simple link between the temperature of seawater and that of the air above it.

However, after analysing years of data from scientific buoys in the Pacific that measure sea and air temperatures simultaneously, the team has found no evidence of a simple link. Instead, the seawater measurements have exaggerated the amount of global warming over the seas, with the real temperature having risen less than half as fast during the 1970s than the standard measurements suggest.

Reporting their findings in the influential journal *Geophysical Research Letters*, the scientists say that the exact cause of the discrepancy is not known. One possibility is that the atmosphere responded faster than the sea to cooling events such as volcanic eruptions.

> **The findings will be seized on by sceptics as more evidence that scientists have little idea about the current rate of global warming, let alone its future rate**

The findings have major implications for the climate change debate because the sea temperature measurements are a key part of global warming calculations. According to the team, replacing the standard seawater data with the appropriate air data produces a big cut in the overall global warming rate during the last 20 years, from around 0.18°C per decade to 0.13°C.

This suggests that the widely-quoted global warming figure used to persuade governments to take action over greenhouse gases exaggerates the true warming rate by almost 40 per cent. The team is now calling for climate experts to switch from seawater data to sea-air temperature measurements.

One member of the team, David Parker, of the Hadley Centre for Climate Prediction and Research at the Met Office, said that the discovery of the discrepancy 'shows we don't understand everything, and that we need better observations – all branches of science are like that'. Yet according to Mr Parker, the new results do not undermine the case for global warming: 'It is raising questions about the interpretation of the sea-surface data.'

Even so, the findings will be seized on by sceptics as more evidence that scientists have little idea about the current rate of global warming, let alone its future rate. Climate experts are still trying to explain why satellites measuring the temperature of the Earth have detected little sign of global warming – despite taking measurements during supposedly the warmest period on record.

Some researchers suspect that the fault may again lie with the ground-based temperature measurements. They say that many of the data come from stations surrounded by growing urban sprawl, whose warmth could give a misleading figure. A study of data taken around Vienna, Austria, between 1951 and 1996 found that the air temperature rose by anything from zero to 0.6°C, depending on precisely where the measurements were made.

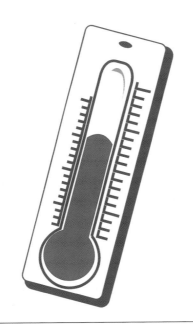

World 'has not got any warmer since 1940'

**By Charles Clover,
Environment Editor**

The world has not warmed since 1940, according to tree rings, coral reef and ice core boreholes, one of the world's leading 'global warming' sceptics told a meeting at the climate change conference.

Prof Fred Singer, a meteorologist at the University of Virginia, used temperature data assembled by James Hanson of Nasa, who first highlighted the problem of climate change, to challenge the findings of the Inter-governmental Panel on the subject which underpin the Kyoto climate treaty.

He said: 'The climate has warmed in the last century but this took place before 1940. The hottest years in America were around 1940. We don't know the cause of the warming but we don't think it was human activity.'

Mr Singer says he has found no evidence suggesting future extreme weather events, such as severe storms or droughts, increases in infectious diseases, or changes to forests and other ecosystems. He accepts there has been an increase in greenhouse gases but believes this has led to 'a greening of the planet, improved agricultural yields and more vigorous forest growth'.

He also accepts evidence from temperature records all over the world that there appears to have been a pronounced warming since 1975, with some of the hottest years in the 1990s. But he says that satellite records of the temperature three miles up, which should show a warming, do not show a warming at all.

He said: 'One explanation is that the satellites are wrong. The other explanation – that is my hypothesis – is that the surface appears to be warming but isn't really warming at all.'

Bob Watson, chairman of the IPCC, has used the surface temperature records of the past 20 years to claim that the 20th century is the warmest for 1,000 years, but Mr Singer disagrees. He places greater faith in the 'proxy' records of temperature, contained in tree rings, ocean sediments, ice cores and so on, which he says show no warming since 1940.

> *No evidence suggesting future extreme weather events, such as severe storms or droughts, increases in infectious diseases, or changes to forests and other ecosystems*

He said: 'Thermometers may not be quite correct. Proxy records say the global temperature has not increased in the past 20 years.' He believes that 'heat islands' caused by urbanisation have distorted thermometer readings. He produced graphs from research conducted by the University of East Anglia and analysis of Greenland ice cores over 100,000 years published in scientific papers to support his point.

Mr Singer is one of several scientists to challenge the broad conclusions of the IPCC, a distillation of the work of 3,000 scientists from most of the leading meteorological institutes. He shared a platform with Richard Coutney, from Britain's Institute of Economic Affairs, who suggested that the summary and conclusions of the IPCC's assessment of the climate had been manipulated by politicians.

Geoff Jenkins, head of the Met Office's Hadley Centre for Climate Prediction and Research, and a leading figure in IPCC, said: 'To say that politicians wrote the summary report of the Inter-govermental Panel on Climate Change is rubbish.' As to satellite data, he said neither this, nor balloon data, showed the expected warming in the upper atmosphere.

'There is warming but the models say it should be the same as the surface. Prof Singer has an issue here that we need to resolve. We don't believe it invalidates the model's predictions of the future. But it's a weakness and we need to sort it out.'

The long-term outlook

Information from the Royal Society for the Protection of Birds (RSPB)

There is disagreement among scientists about the seriousness of global warming. Most scientists agree that the global temperature is rising. They do not agree on more specific elements of the issue: How much will it warm up? What will happen if it does warm up? How far are humans responsible? What should we do to stop it?

Scientists believe that if we go on producing gases at the rate we do now, it is likely that the Earth's average temperature will rise by about 0.3 degrees C every ten years. This does not sound much, and it might be pleasant to have hotter summers in Britain, but it could have a huge effect on all living things on Earth. Changes in global temperature of the kind predicted could have considerable effects on rainfall and wind, as well as warmer weather. They can also affect ocean currents, which can greatly affect the weather, and the unusual weather experienced during El Niño is an example of the effect the ocean has on the weather.

Sea-level rise is another effect of climate change. This will happen as temperatures rise, and warm water will occupy more space than cold water, flooding low-lying areas (sea-level rise is not primarily due to melting polar ice caps). Again, there is disagreement as to how much the sea level will rise. Many of the world's cities and much agricultural land are in the threatened zones.

As the global temperature rises, the distribution of plants and animals will be changed. Again, the consequences are unpredictable, but countries that now have rich agricultural land could find these less productive: others may find poor areas improved.

Wildlife already faces a number of threats and many species and habitats are vulnerable to human activities. Although we are not sure how climate change will affect wildlife, it is clear that its impact will make things worse.

Many types of wildlife depend on natural signals, such as temperature or day length, to time their life cycles, and if some of these signals alter due to climate change, the timing of life cycles will change. A study of birds across the UK from 1971 to 1995 shows that 63% of the species are showing a tendency to nest earlier. Twenty species of UK breeding bird are laying their first egg an average of nine days earlier than they did 20 years ago.

Wildlife already faces a number of threats and many species and habitats are vulnerable to human activities

---

Most scientists accept that global warming will cause wildlife to shift northwards, or to move higher in altitude: this is what happened, very slowly, after previous Ice Ages, as the Earth warmed up again. However, some species may not be able to move if climate change is so rapid that they, or the other species on which they depend for food, cannot move into new areas where the climate is suitable for them. Plants, for example, may not be able to disperse themselves fast enough to keep pace with the shift in location of their optimal climate conditions.

Animals that migrate may be affected by global warming. The success of migration depends upon the right places being available at the right times of year, with the right food needed to complete the migration. If the links in the chain of areas vital to migration are damaged, migrants' survival is threatened. In the US, Delaware Bay is a vital feeding ground for knots, which feed on the eggs of the horseshoe crab. Eggs are a vital fuel source to sustain the knots in the Arctic. Any changes in the timing and availability of eggs or the arrival of the knots will have an adverse impact on the success of the birds in reaching their destination. Food supplies at staging areas during the spring migration may affect not only a bird's ability to reach its destination, but also its breeding success, as is the case for some Arctic nesting geese.

What does global warming mean for the UK?

Scientists believe we will have more dry summers, like the drought of 1995 which cost the UK water, agriculture and insurance industries millions of pounds. Mountain-top habitats like those in the Cairngorms may be lost, along with their special birds, such as ptarmigans and dotterels. We could lose some 40 plant species. The threat from sea-level rise means that birds that live on the coasts could be threatened. Wintering wildfowl and wading birds on estuaries will be threatened by the loss of intertidal feeding areas, caused by increased erosion of the shoreline, particularly where there are sea defences.

Other common misconceptions

The greenhouse effect is caused because heat cannot escape from the earth because it cannot find the holes in the ozone layer.

Air pollution

A great variety of substances are released into our environment. Many of these are waste products from industry, agriculture or private homes, that enter the air, rivers, the sea and the land. Occasionally, substances may escape by accident. Where these substances are in amounts that do harm to the environment, we regard them as pollutants.

The RSPB is often asked for information about pollution and how it affects birds. This is a difficult question to answer, because many of the effects of pollution do not show in an obvious way or kill birds outright. They build up slowly, so that we only notice gradually that the numbers of particular bird species are decreasing. It is almost impossible to say – except in a major incident like an oil spill – that an individual bird has died as a result of pollution. However, pollution can affect birds through the food-chains. For example, there may be less food for birds.

Pollution of the atmosphere has been a problem since the Industrial Revolution. We pollute the air with smoke and fumes from fires, factories and power stations, and from cars and other vehicles. These are some of the main air pollution problems:

Sulphur dioxide

Sulphur dioxide gas is produced when materials containing sulphur are burned. It comes from industry, power stations, the burning of fossil fuels, and from car exhausts. The infamous London 'smogs' in the 1950s contained large amounts of sulphur dioxide from burning coal. Sulphur dioxide affects the respiratory (breathing) system of humans, particularly when combined with smoke. It also dissolves in rainwater, causing acid rain (see below).

Sulphur dioxide is still produced by burning smokeless fuels and oil. Wildlife varies in its sensitivity to this pollution – some species are very sensitive, while others are very tolerant. Some plants called lichens are particularly vulnerable. They can be useful indicators of the amount of pollution in the atmosphere.

Nitrogen oxides

Nitrogen oxide comes from vehicles and factories. It is a toxic and irritant gas, which affects the respiratory system of humans. When nitrogen dioxide dissolves in rainwater it causes acid rain. Nitrogen oxide reacts with sunlight to produce a gas called ozone, which can be hazardous to humans and wildlife.

Carbon dioxide

Carbon dioxide occurs naturally in the atmosphere with other gases such as nitrogen, oxygen and water vapour. The carbon dioxide and water vapour act as a sort of 'blanket' and trap the heat from the sun in the atmosphere, keeping the Earth warm. This is called the 'greenhouse effect'. Carbon dioxide is often called a 'greenhouse gas'.

Human activities, such as the burning of fossil fuels (coal, oil and gas), produce carbon dioxide. It is produced when anything organic is burned, and comes from power stations, factories, cars and other vehicles, and from burning down forests. These human activities are adding lots more carbon dioxide to the Earth's atmosphere, and the atmosphere is changing. The extra carbon dioxide causes more heat to be held within the atmosphere. This

– YOU'RE COPING WITH POLLUTION?

... I USED TO BE A FLOCK...

is popularly known as 'global warming', and is leading to changes in the world's climate.

Particulates

Particulates is the word used to describe solid particles in the air. You can see them as a dark dirty coating on surfaces in towns. Smoke from burning coal has been a threat to human health. During the 1950s certain weather conditions used to cause smogs in our cities. Since the introduction of the Clean Air Acts, cities are much cleaner.

Carbon particles (which look like tiny pieces of soot) come mainly from lorries and buses that use diesel. They may cause respiratory problems in humans. Motor vehicles create more and more pollution in towns.

Carbon monoxide and lead

Motor exhaust fumes contain a poisonous gas, carbon monoxide. Levels of this gas may be high in heavy slow-moving traffic in built-up areas. When it is breathed in, it gets into the bloodstream, where it combines with the red pigment haemoglobin. This blocks the uptake of oxygen and can be fatal.

Lead is a poisonous heavy metal. It has been added to petrol and paint, and it was used as lead weights for fishing, and as shot for shooting wildfowl. Lead poisoning affects the health and survival of animals and humans. Exhaust fumes contain lead. Breathing in a lot of fumes can be dangerous. Lead in the environment is beginning to decline. There are now stricter controls in the use of lead in paints and in field sports (see the RSPB factsheet on Freshwater Pollution), and more cars use unleaded fuel. Leaded petrol is banned throughout the European Union from year 2000.

Further reading

The RSPB has produced a series of factsheets on pollution including *Air pollution*; *Land pollution*; *The greenhouse effect, climate change and wildlife*. They have also compiled a reading list of references on pollution. All these are available from Wildlife Enquiries on 01767 680551.

Global pollution and climate change

One hundred years ago, Claude Monet painted scenes of London through its smoggy atmosphere. That was local pollution. What is relatively new and even more worrying is global pollution – that is pollution emitted locally that has global effects.

The first example that arose in the 1980s was damage to the Earth's ozone layer. International action through the Montreal Protocol has been taken to phase out the use of the chemicals responsible although full recovery of the ozone layer will take at least a century.

Another example is pollution that leads to global warming and climate change. This article will explain how this pollution occurs, how it leads to climate change, what the damaging impacts might be and what action can be taken to reduce them.

The greenhouse effect

First we need to understand how the Earth's temperature is regulated. The Earth absorbs the heat energy of sunshine mainly at the surface. To maintain a steady temperature, a balancing amount of energy is then radiated upwards from the surface at longer, infrared, wavelengths. Some of the gases in the atmosphere which are present naturally, particularly water vapour, carbon dioxide and methane, absorb some of this infrared radiation so acting as 'blankets' over the surface. A close control is thereby kept on global temperature with the Earth's surface nearly 30°C warmer than it would otherwise be, providing an average climate for the Earth very suitable for human life. It is known as the 'greenhouse effect' because the glass in a greenhouse possesses similar properties to the atmosphere.

Increases in the amount of gases such as carbon dioxide in the atmosphere are occurring because of emissions from human activities such as the burning of fossil fuels (coal, oil

and gas) or through deforestation. These increases are sufficient to seriously perturb the natural, ecological processes that control the Earth's temperature. They are leading on average to increased warming.

Most rapid change in last 10,000 years

The climate record over many thousands of years can be built up by analysing the composition of the ice, and the air trapped in the ice, obtained from different depths from cores drilled from the Antarctic or Greenland ice-caps.

Currently the Earth's climate is in a long-term warm phase which began when the last ice age ended about 20,000 years ago; the last warm period was about 120,000 years ago. The main triggers for ice ages have been the small regular variations in the geometry of the Earth's orbit about the sun which affect the distribution of solar radiation at the Earth's surface. The next ice age is expected to begin in about 50,000 years' time.

A strong correlation exists between atmospheric temperature

Over the past 200 years human activities have increased the amount of carbon dioxide in the atmosphere by over 30%

---

and carbon dioxide content. This is partly because the amount of carbon dioxide in the atmosphere is dependent on factors strongly connected to the average temperature. Also, the carbon dioxide content in its turn influences the temperature through the greenhouse effect.

Over the past 200 years human activities have increased the amount of carbon dioxide in the atmosphere by over 30% – well beyond the range of its natural variation during the last million years or more. If the increase continues and if adequate action is not taken to stem it, the atmospheric carbon dioxide content will reach double its pre-industrial value during the 21st century. As a result the average rate of warming of the climate is expected to be greater than at any time during the last 10,000 years. This is not necessarily bad; some communities may experience a net benefit. But many ecosystems and humans will find it difficult to adjust to this rate of change.

International agreement about the science

Although there is a lot of uncertainty concerning the detail, the basic science underlying global warming and climate change is well understood and is not in question. Hundreds of scientists from over fifty nations, including the world's leading scientists in the field, have contributed as authors or reviewers to the assessments of the Intergovernmental Panel on Climate Change (IPCC). Because of the uncertainties it is easy either to exaggerate the possible impacts to calamitous proportions or to suggest that too little is known to justify any action.

What the IPCC has done is explain clearly what is known together with the major uncertainties. Then, taking account of all relevant scientific data, best estimates have been provided of climate change and its impact over the coming century, and the options for mitigating action. In the paragraphs that follow are summarised a few of the IPCC's main findings that will form the agenda for the years ahead.

Climate variability and recent warming

The average air temperature near the Earth's surface over the past century shows a lot of variability due to influences such as volcanic eruptions, variations in the heat from the sun and natural variations that occur in the absence of any external influences. The increase since the 1970s is considered to be largely due to the increase of greenhouse gases (especially carbon dioxide) because of human activities. In terms of global average temperature the 1990s have been particularly warm. Not only is 1998 the warmest year on record, the first eight months of 1998 were themselves the warmest of those months on record; a striking statistic. If carbon dioxide concentration increases during the 21st century to more than twice its pre-industrial value then calculations show that global average temperature will rise by about 2.5°C (range of uncertainty estimated as 1.5 to 4.5°C). When compared with the temperature changes we commonly experience a rise of 2.5°C does not seem very large. But remember it is a rise in the average annual tempera-ture over the whole globe. Between the middle of an ice age and the warm periods in between ice ages, the global average temperature changed by only about 5 or 6°C. So a 2.5°C rise represents about half an 'ice age' in terms of climate change. For this to occur in less than 100 years, as we have already noted, is very rapid change.

So far we've presented climate change in terms of average temperature. But we are more likely to experience change in terms of extreme weather such as floods, droughts and storms. Such extremes are continually occurring because of the large natural variability of climate. As human communities especially with their increasing populations become increasingly vulnerable to such extremes, a key question is whether these extremes will become more intense with global warming. It is to that question we will now turn.

The impacts of global warming

In some locations, the impacts of global warming may be positive. For some crops, increased carbon dioxide aids growth and at high northern latitudes winters will be less cold and the growing season longer. However, because humans and ecosystems have adapted closely to the current climate, most climate change, especially if the change is fast, is likely to have negative impacts. The main impacts are likely to be changes in sea level, rainfall, and temperature extremes.

First, largely because of thermal expansion of ocean water and accelerated melting of glaciers, sea level is likely to rise by about half a metre by 2100. Sea defences in many coastal regions will need to be improved, albeit at considerable cost. However, such adaptation is not possible for countries with large river deltas such as Bangladesh, southern China and Egypt and for many islands in the Pacific and Indian Oceans.

A second major impact of global warming is likely to be on water supplies. Warming of the Earth's surface means greater evaporation and, on average, a higher water vapour content in the atmosphere. Because the latent heat of condensation is the main energy source for the atmosphere's circulation this leads to a more vigorous hydrological cycle. In many areas, heavy rainfall may become heavier while semi-arid areas may receive less rainfall. There will be more frequent and more intense floods or droughts, especially in sub-tropical areas, which are vulnerable to such events. In many places, water is rapidly becoming a critical resource; a former Secretary General of the United Nations said that he expected the next war to be about water not oil!

Floods and droughts already cause more deaths, misery and economic damage than any other type of disasters. Any increase in their frequency or intensity could be the most damaging impacts of global climate change.

Studies of food supplies in a globally warmed world suggest that the world-wide quantity of available food supply might not be greatly affected. Some regions might be able to grow more while others grow less. However, the distribution of food production will change, not least because of changed water availability.

The regions likely to be adversely affected are those in developing countries in the sub-tropics. Here there are rapidly increasing populations and agricultural production will become inadequate to meet local needs. Considering food supplies, sea-level rise and the incidence of floods and droughts, a recent carefully researched study (N. Myers, 1995 – *Environmental Exodus*, Climate Institute, Washington DC) has estimated that there may be 150 million environmental refugees by 2050.

Other likely impacts are on human health (increased heat stress and more widespread vector borne diseases such as malaria) and on the health of some ecosystems (e.g. forests) which will not be able to adapt rapidly enough to match the rate of climate change.

International political action

At the Earth Summit held in Rio de Janeiro in 1992, around 160 nations agreed the Framework Convention on Climate Change (FCCC). Three widely accepted principles will govern the international agreements needed to meet the threat of climate change.

- Precautionary Principle: already clearly imbedded in the FCCC. This states that the existence of uncertainty should not preclude the taking of appropriate action. The objective for such action is simply stated as the stabilisation of the concentrations of greenhouse gases (such as carbon dioxide) in the atmosphere in ways that allow also for necessary economic development.
- Polluter Pays Principle: which implies the imposition of measures such as carbon taxes or carbon trading.

- Principle of Equity (both Intergenerational and International): which is the most difficult to apply. However, a proposal of the Global Commons Institute, that is being widely discussed, applies the second and third principles by allowing for the eventual allocation of carbon emissions to nations on an equal per capita basis while also allowing for emissions trading.

A start was made at Kyoto in 1997 with agreement to a Protocol (yet to be ratified) requiring developed nations to reduce their emissions of greenhouse gases by the year 2010 by 5% on average compared to 1990. This is a first step, hopefully demonstrating commitment by the developed world. Necessary post-Kyoto action, however, will be more demanding. Developing countries who wish to industrialise also need to join the action; in this they will need substantial encouragement (e.g. appropriate technology development and transfer) to enable them to develop industrially without vast increases in carbon dioxide emissions.

To meet likely FCCC requirements for carbon dioxide stabilisation, the rate of increase of global emissions must first be substantially slowed; then there must be reductions in these emissions to well below 1990 levels before 2100. Studies show that the necessary action, if carefully planned and phased, is likely to cost less than 1% of the Global World Product, much less than the likely cost of damage and adaptation if there is no action at all.

This will require rapid development and deployment of appropriate technology and a great deal of determination on the part of the world community.

Action to mitigate climate change

To mitigate the effects of global climate change, action is required to reduce the human-induced emissions of carbon dioxide. This has large implications, for the energy sector in particular. Technology is already available for much of what is required, for instance to generate and use energy much more efficiently and to develop non fossil fuel energy sources such as solar, wind, water, biomass and other renewables.

Action can also be taken to increase the sinks which remove carbon dioxide from the atmosphere (e.g. by reducing deforestation and increasing forestation or by direct sequestration of carbon dioxide) and to reduce methane emissions from, for example, leakage from mines and landfill sites. The main role of governments and world agencies will be to stimulate markets, to encourage the development and use of the most appropriate clean technologies.

A challenge for everybody

- for scientists, to provide better information about likely climate change and its various local impacts;
- for governments, to set the necessary framework;
- for business and industry, to seize the opportunities for innovation and use of 'clean' technologies and
- for all communities and individuals in the world, to support the action being taken and contribute to it.

What the individual can do

- ensure maximum energy efficiency in the home (over 25% of CO_2 emissions are from domestic energy use) through good heat insulation and through the use of high efficiency appliances (e.g. low energy light bulbs, Grade A or B appliances).
- ensure maximum energy saving – do not overheat rooms and turn off lights when not required.
- support, where possible, the provision of energy from renewable sources; e.g. purchase 'green' electricity now that this option is available.
- use public transport, and walk and cycle where possible, and use a fuel-efficient car (over 25% of CO_2 emissions come from transport).
- consider the environment when shopping; e.g. buy goods produced with low energy use and products that originate from renewable sources.
- through the democratic process, encourage local and national government to deliver policies that properly take the environment into account.

Credits

This briefing has been prepared for the John Ray Initiative by Sir John Houghton. Thanks are due to Dr Bruce Callander, Prof John Twidell and the JRI Trustees for helpful comments.

© The John Ray Initiative

Counting the cost of climate change

Information from Greenpeace

Autumn 2000 brought extreme weather to Britain. Flooding was the worst and most widespread in 100 years. More than 3,000 homes were flooded across Britain and our transport system was paralysed. Extreme weather is no longer simply a natural event. The current changes to our climate cannot now be separated from the impact of fossil fuel pollution. Unless we break our addiction to fossil fuels like oil and coal we are set to experience even greater changes.

Counting the cost
10% of the population (some 5 million people) and 12% of agricultural land in Britain are at risk from flooding. This accounts for £200 billion worth of property and land worth more than £7 billion.

Insurance
In 1999, weather-related claims cost the insurance industry £860 million. The 2000 autumn storms cost industry an estimated £500 million. According to the Association of British Insurers, insurance premiums are likely to increase if recent weather patterns continue. Subsidence – on the increase as summers get hotter and drier because of climate change – has already caused a steady rise in household insurance premiums over the last 15 years.

Flood defences
The UK spends £200 million a year building flood defences. A study commissioned by the Ministry of Agriculture, Fisheries and Foods predicts that if investment in flood defences continues to be limited to current levels, the yearly cost of flood damage will reach £1.8 billion.

Housing
Surveyors estimate that the value of properties built on the flood plains

or near rivers and coastal areas could plunge by as much as 25%. Government estimates suggest that overhauling residential and commercial building methods to cope with flood 'alleviation' and other extreme weather effects could cost £26 billion over the next 30 years. The rising costs are likely to be met through higher property prices.

Future impacts
In the last ten years, the UK has suffered four of the hottest summers since records began. The UN Intergovernmental Panel on Climate Change predicts a rapid increase in global warming and severe weather as a consequence of human activities such as burning fossil fuels.

A new EU report backs this up, concluding that Britain will become warmer and wetter. Winters will be warmer with more flooding, tornadoes and intense rainstorms. The south of England faces long droughts interspersed with violent flooding.

The Gulf Stream, which channels warm sea water from the Gulf of Mexico to the Atlantic coast of northern Europe, currently keeps Britain warmer than other countries

this far north. A minor rise in temperature in the Arctic could disrupt the Gulf Stream, resulting in dramatic changes to Britain's weather and climate.

As rising sea levels of between 4mm and 6mm a year threaten the coast of Britain, coastal defence may cease to be either effective or economical. Low-lying farmland and coastal towns risk disappearing altogether.

The Thames barrier provides temporary protection for homes at risk around London. It has only been used 30 times since it was built. The Environment Agency expects that by 2080 it may have to be used 300 days a year.

The road ahead
Greenpeace calls for a massive Government programme for renewable energy and green fuels. Such a programme would:
- help reduce the risk of increased extreme weather from climate change
- reduce health impacts from fossil fuel pollution build a new energy technology industry for Britain.

© Greenpeace

Climate change

Ever since human beings began to walk the Earth, we have been dominated by the climate. Information from WWF-UK

Introduction

Our tribal ancestors were constantly on the move, following large mammals on their migratory routes and trying to avoid extremes of cold, rain and heat. But in due course they settled, and learned to adapt to the climate that ruled them.

Today, whoever and wherever we are, the climate still dictates the way we live. The cities we build, the clothes we wear, the kind of homes we live in, the food we eat, even how we behave . . . all are based on the weather patterns it produces locally.

What is climate change?

The Earth's climate naturally changes over long time periods. Over the 4.5 billion years that the planet has existed, we have swung between cold and warm periods. Ice ages have come and gone, and have lasted for up to 100,000 years. They have been followed by shorter, warmer periods, one of which we are in at the moment: the Earth's average temperature is around 4°C hotter than it was during the last ice age some 13,000 years ago.

But recently, the changes have accelerated so much that it is now also half a degree warmer than it was during the 1860s. That may not seem a very big increase at all, but it's huge for a relatively short timespan of 135 years.

And there is one major difference between previous periods of warmth and this one. In the past, they have been due to natural events and have taken thousands of years to evolve, so species have had time to adapt – but this time it is caused by the world's 5.8 billion human beings. Data from ice cores suggest that we are living in the warmest century for 600 years – and we certainly know that the final two decades of the 20th century are the hottest on record. We're turning up the planet's thermostat so fast that nature can no longer cope.

What are the causes?

Every time we turn on a light switch, use a computer, watch television or cook a meal, we are creating carbon dioxide (CO_2) – which is not only a naturally-occurring gas crucial to our survival, but also the main contributor to climate change.

The electricity we use is generated by power stations, most of which burn 'fossil fuels' – so called because they have been created over millions of years by the slow underground decay of vegetation and other living matter. We also burn fossil fuels in other ways – every time we drive a car, for example.

The three fossil fuels we burn are coal, oil and natural gas, each of which has hydrogen and carbon in its makeup. When they are burned, these components mix with oxygen in the atmosphere. The result is carbon dioxide.

Carbon dioxide and other greenhouse gases occur naturally and form a blanket around the Earth, trapping heat that would otherwise escape into space. The heat rebounds onto the Earth's surface, and the planet's temperature rises – creating what is commonly called the 'greenhouse effect'. But we have been pumping additional CO_2 into the atmosphere for 200 years, thus intensifying the greenhouse effect and increasing the Earth's temperature. To make things worse, we have also increased the levels of other natural greenhouse gases, such as methane and nitrous oxide – and if that's not enough, we are now adding ever-increasing quantities of industrial gases which themselves contribute to the powerful greenhouse effect.

At the speed our climate is changing, the world will soon be warmer than at any time in the last 10,000 years. We're turning up the planet's thermostat so fast that nature can no longer cope. Such a warming will also have widespread impacts on climatic conditions all over the globe, causing more droughts, storms, floods and other weather extremes.

Trees are great natural store-houses of carbon dioxide, some retaining it for a century or more. Over the years, billions of tonnes of CO_2 in the atmosphere are absorbed by the world's forests, and this helps balance the climate. But when forests are cut down and burned – as they frequently are when being cleared for agricultural land or for town expansion – the gas retained over a lifetime is released back into the air. The damage is made worse by the fact that because the forests are not replaced, there are fewer trees to absorb CO_2 when more are needed than ever before.

Melting glaciers

Nowhere is safe from the effects of climate change. Glaciers are already melting in places as far apart as Switzerland and New Zealand, bringing with them avalanches, soil erosion and dramatic changes to river flows. Snow is melting on great mountain ranges such as the Alps and the Andes – making the risk of serious flooding even worse.

Away from the mountains, the oceans and seas are warming, causing coral to die and putting many marine creatures at risk. Warmer water occupies more space than cold water, so as the oceans gradually heat up, they also expand – threatening to submerge many parts of the world including some 300 Pacific islands, and wetlands as far afield as Argentina and Bangladesh, Nigeria and the United States.

Unusual weather conditions can put many species of animals and plants at risk. The danger now is that if those conditions become perm-anent or extreme, numerous plants and animals will simply not recover. Hurricanes, storms and flooding would become more common in some parts of the world, and severe droughts in other areas.

Cold kills germs and disease-bearing insects such as the mosquito. But as the world warms up, germs, bacteria and other carriers will multiply. Longer and hotter heatwaves caused by climate change are creating perfect breeding conditions for rats and other pests, and diseases such as plague and malaria are on the increase.

Scientists around the world are telling us urgently that climate change is serious. But they also believe that it is not too late – if we act now.

What can be done – by government and industry?

Most of the blame for greenhouse gas emissions lies with people in the prosperous developed world who produce almost five billion tonnes of CO_2 and other gases each year. At a United Nations conference in Kyoto in 1997, legally binding targets were drawn up that should result in developed countries reducing their greenhouse gas emissions by just over five per cent by 2012. While this is not enough to avoid the risk of dangerous climate change, at least it is a first step. In addition to this Kyoto commitment, the British government has also set itself a separate voluntary target – to emit 20 per cent less carbon dioxide in 2010 than in 1990.

If they are to achieve their targets, governments everywhere must take immediate action that will lead to cleaner energy production, more efficient energy use, better and more efficient public transport, responsible industrial and agri-cultural practices, careful forestry procedures and far more effective waste management. We must invest in buildings that use solar energy and are well insulated, and in vehicles powered by alternative fuels. And all the time, we must plant more trees in our towns and cities: they

provide shade, keep temperatures down, and absorb CO_2.

All these things will help us control climate change.

There will be other benefits from these measures. People and businesses can save money, and the negative health effects associated with air pollution from traffic and industry can be reduced.

What can be done – by you?

Everyone can do something to reduce the threat of climate change. Cutting out just one car journey a week will help. So will turning the central heating down by merely 1°C. Using insulation, energy-saving electrical appliances and efficient light bulbs will make a difference, too: some compact fluorescent bulbs can last 10,000 hours and use only 20 per cent of the electricity consumed by ordinary bulbs. You can also choose an electricity company that offers a green tariff by supplying electricity from renewable energy sources.

If everyone pressed for better public transport – then used it – we would save millions of litres of fuel. Other simple actions that will benefit the planet include re-using and re-cycling paper, glass, aluminium, tin and clothing, and not buying disposable products (especially plastic) or anything with a lot of unnecessary packaging.

Climate change has come and gone in natural cycles since the early days of the planet. But this time it has been brought about by human abuse of our fragile environ-ment. We are the cause of the problem . . . but we can also be the solution.

Do we plunder the Earth – or make sure we protect it for future generations? The choice is ours.

Please help WWF continue its vital work by becoming a member, making a donation, or joining a volunteers' group.

• The above information is from the WWF-UK web site which can be found at www.wwf-uk.org Alternatively see page 41 for their address details.

© WWF-UK

Climate change – the UK programme

Action is needed to tackle climate change

Climate change is one of the most serious threats facing the world's environment, economy and society. But if we all act, the world can avoid its worst effects. The devastating floods, droughts and storms we have seen in the UK and across the world in recent years show all too clearly how vulnerable we are to climate extremes and how devastating they can be. And we have been warned that things will get worse. We have to take practical action to deal with flooding and severe weather. But we also need to tackle climate change by cutting the greenhouse gas emissions that cause it.

Responding to the challenge

As a result of the Kyoto Protocol, developed countries have agreed that they will cut their overall emissions of greenhouse gases by 5.2% below 1990 levels by 2008-2012. For the first time, these targets will be legally binding and countries have different targets to reflect their circumstances.

The UK's leading role

Following Kyoto, the UK's target is to cut its emissions by 12.5% below 1990 levels by 2008-2012. But the Government and the devolved administrations are convinced that the UK can and should go further. The Kyoto Protocol is only the first step. In the longer term, bigger cuts world-wide – perhaps 60% or more – will be needed. There will also be many benefits for the UK from taking early action to cut our emissions. This approach is supported by many other stakeholders, including business and local authorities.

The Government and the devolved administrations have therefore set a domestic goal to go further than the Kyoto commitment and cut the UK's emissions of carbon dioxide by 20% below 1990 levels by 2010.

This programme will deliver significant cuts in emissions

The UK's programme is a significant contribution to the global response to climate change. It sets out a strategic, far-reaching package of policies and measures across all sectors of the economy. We estimate that it could cut the UK's greenhouse gases by 23% below 1990 levels by 2010. This means that carbon dioxide emissions could be reduced by 19% by 2010 and that we could achieve the 20% domestic goal.

Working in partnership with other key stakeholders

The programme is supported by many other stakeholders. Not only have they worked closely with the Government and the devolved administrations to develop it. They will also be crucial in delivering it.

They recognise the benefits that the policies and measures offer including:

- improved energy efficiency and lower costs for businesses and householders;
- more employment opportunities through the development of new, environmental technologies;
- a better transport system;
- better local air quality;
- less fuel poverty; and
- improved international competitiveness for the UK.

The programme sets out how much we have achieved during the last decade, and how much we intend to achieve in the future, through action by businesses, local authorities, other organisations and individuals. The programme highlights good examples and aims to inspire others to take similar action.

This information provides a summary of the main areas of action and key facts and figures relating to the programme.

Why should we act?

The world is getting warmer. Global temperatures rose by 0.6°C during the last century,

- they are forecast to rise about 3°C during this century; and
- the 1990s included seven of the ten warmest years on record and 1998 was the warmest year in a 140-year record.

Average temperatures have also risen in the UK. In England, four of the five warmest years in a 340-year

record were experienced in the 1990s and 1999 was the joint warmest year ever.

The world faces major impacts
The rate at which the climate is changing will affect the world in extreme and unpredictable ways. Climate change brings with it huge costs to the economy, environment and society, including:

- temperature increases, drought and flooding will affect people's health and way of life, and cause the irreversible loss of many species of plants and animals;
- rising sea levels threaten the existence of some small island states and put millions of people at risk; and
- in the UK, rising seas threaten our coastal communities and environment, and higher temperatures, increased and more intense rainfall will bring droughts and flooding.

Avoiding the worst impacts
We cannot avoid some climate change. Greenhouse gases which have already built up in the atmosphere mean that some rise in temperature is inevitable. So we need to consider what steps we should take to cope with the effects. But the worst effects of climate change can be avoided if the world begins now to cut its emissions of the greenhouse gases that cause climate change. This is a major challenge and the scale of the changes needed must not be underestimated.

The world is responding
Countries around the world are taking action through the United Nations Framework Convention on Climate Change, which was agreed at the Earth Summit in Rio de Janeiro in 1992. Under the Convention, all developed countries agreed to aim to return their greenhouse gas emissions to 1990 levels by 2000. The UK will be one of a small number of OECD countries who will meet this target, as its emissions in 2000 are projected to be about 13.5% below 1990 levels.

These commitments can only be a first step in the fight against climate change. Climate prediction models show that much deeper cuts in emissions will be needed globally – perhaps 60% or more – if we are to avoid the worst effects of climate change. The Kyoto Protocol was designed to address this need, and is an important stage in what will be a long-term process.

For the first time, developed countries agreed to take on legally binding targets to cut their emissions. If delivered, these targets will reduce developed countries' emissions of greenhouse gases by 5.2% below 1990 levels over the period 2008-2012. Developed countries also know that tougher targets are likely to be needed beyond 2010, and that developing countries will need to be part of the long-term global response to climate change.

As a result of the Kyoto Protocol and an agreement between European member states, the UK has a target to reduce its greenhouse emissions by 12.5% below 1990 levels by 2008-2012. It also has a domestic goal to reduce its carbon dioxide emissions by 20% below 1990 levels by 2010.

The UK's climate change programme
The UK has already made major cuts in its emissions
Projections show that action already taken in the UK is currently expected to cut emissions by around 15% below 1990 levels in 2010. The projections include the effect of some policies that have been introduced since Kyoto, such as the climate change levy and the 10% renewables target. The projections also show the gap to the 20% domestic goal and illustrate that more action is needed if emissions are to continue falling after 2010.

What further action is needed?
The UK's climate change programme sets out the UK's response to the world-wide call for action. The Government and the devolved administrations are leading the way in outlining a strategic, far-reaching programme that:

- helps people to understand why we need to tackle climate change;
- explains how the international community is responding and describes the leading role the UK has played internationally and in Europe;
- will deliver the UK's legally binding target under the Kyoto Protocol. It could cut our greenhouse gas emissions by an estimated 23% below 1990 levels by 2010. This means that carbon dioxide emissions alone could be reduced by an estimated 19% below 1990 levels by 2010. Together with policies where the impact has not been quantified, this could also achieve the domestic goal;
- sets out a package of cost-effective, flexible policies and measures in which all sectors of the UK's economy and all parts of the UK play their part. The package will safeguard and enhance the UK's competitiveness and deliver

wider benefits through lower energy costs for businesses and people; less fuel poverty; improved air quality in our towns and cities; reduced risk to health; and new business and export opportunities;

- responds to the need for action to cut emissions in the longer term by putting in place policies that give clear signals about the changes that will be needed and ensure the UK moves towards a more sustainable, low carbon economy;

- builds on and develops the partnerships and the action being taken by many other stake-holders. The programme sets a clear framework and direction that will enable and empower key players to do what they can to reduce emissions; and

- outlines the action the Government has started to take to prepare the UK to adapt to the impacts of a changing climate.

Policies and measures in the package

The climate change programme sets out a substantial, integrated package of policies and measures to:

- improve business' use of energy, stimulate investment and cut costs:
  - the climate change levy package, which includes challenging improvement targets for energy intensive sectors through climate change agreements, and additional support for energy efficiency measures in the business sector;
  - a domestic emissions trading scheme, with Government support of £30 million in 2003-2004 to kick-start the scheme by providing a financial incentive for companies to take on binding emission reduction targets;
  - establishment of a new Carbon Trust, which will recycle £130 million of climate change levy receipts to accelerate the take-up of cost-effective, low carbon technologies and other measures by business and levy players;
  - exemption of good quality CHP (combined heat and power) and renewable sources of

electricity from the climate change levy;
  - energy labels, standards and other product-related measures designed to deliver 'market transformation' in the energy efficiency of lighting, appliances and other key traded goods; and
  - Integrated Pollution Prevention and Control.

- stimulate new, more efficient sources of power generation:
  - electricity suppliers will be obliged to increase the proportion of electricity provided by renewable sources to 10% by 2010, subject to the cost to consumers being acceptable; and
  - a target to at least double the UK's CHP capacity by 2010.

- cut emissions from the transport sector;
  - European-level agreements with car manufacturers to improve the average fuel efficiency on new cars by at least 25% by 2008-2009, backed up by changes to vehicle excise duty and the reform of company car taxation; and
  - the 10 Year Plan: £180 billion of investment and public spending on transport over the next ten years to cut congestion and reduce pollution.

- promote better energy efficiency in the domestic sector, saving householders money:
  - a new Energy Efficiency Commitment (successor to the Energy Efficiency Standards of Performance), through which

electricity and gas suppliers will help their domestic customers, particularly the elderly and those on low incomes, to save energy and cut their fuel bills;
  - the New Home Energy Efficiency Scheme in England, similar schemes for Wales and Northern Ireland and, in Scotland, the Warm Deal Initiative;
  - an Affordable Warmth Programme developed in conjunction with Transco to facilitate the installation of efficient gas central heating systems and insulation in a million homes;
  - the promotion of new community heating and upgrading of existing systems; and
  - more efficient lighting, heating and other appliances.

- improve the energy efficiency requirements of the Building Regulations;

- continue cutting emissions from agriculture by:
  - better countryside management;
  - cutting fertiliser use;
  - protecting and enhancing forests; and
  - better energy efficiency.

- ensure the public sector takes a leading role by:
  - new targets for improving energy management of public buildings;
  - energy efficiency targets for local authorities, schools and hospitals; and
  - developing green travel plans.

Cutting emissions in the longer term

We need a long-term response to tackle climate change, including a fundamental shift in the way we generate and use energy over the coming century. There are no easy solutions. The Government does not have all the answers and it wants a national debate on how the UK might make the transformation to a low carbon economy, drawing on the advice of experts to look at technological options for the future and the scope for significantly changing patterns of demand and consumer behaviour. The Government plans to review the option for longer-term energy choices, considering the scale of emission reduction that might be needed and the scope and cost of low carbon or energy efficiency options that could be used.

The programme begins to lay the foundation for more fundamental changes in the years to come. Many of its policies and measures will deliver cuts beyond 2010:

- the new strategy on renewable energy; the Government has announced substantial new capital grants to support offshore wind and energy crop installations. £89 million is to be made available from the Government and the New Opportunities Fund. An additional £12 million over three years will be available as planting grants for energy crops;
- action to ensure fair access to the electricity distribution networks as numerous small and scattered sources of electricity supply come into the market;
- market mechanisms, such as the climate change levy and emissions trading, which will encourage industry to invest in low carbon technologies and research and development;
- developing a new co-ordination framework for the development of these new technologies;
- changes to the planning system which will influence development patterns and reduce the need to travel; and
- a significant expansion of programmes to increase the penetration of the next generation of fuel efficient technologies and to overcome barriers to their use.

Adapting to a climate change

The UK needs to adapt to the predicted impacts of climate change including sea-level rise, droughts and more intense rainfall. Extreme weather events, such as severe flooding, will become more common. The programme examines likely impacts on the UK, considers how central and local government, businesses and other organisations might start adapting and suggests priorities for the UK.

The Government has begun to take action to prepare the UK for climate change. Work to predict and assess the impacts on the UK is being enhanced so that its adaptation response can be well targeted. The Government has announced that it:

- is reviewing its approach to development in flood risk areas with the Environment Agency;
- will issue fresh planning guidance to local authorities;
- is providing significant extra funding for flood and coastal defences; and
- is taking action to prepare for the effects climate change is likely to have on water resources, buildings, biodiversity, and agriculture and forestry.

© Crown Copyright 2000 (Department of the Environment, Transport and the Regions (DETR)

Planet savers

Information from Friends of the Earth

Here are five easy ways to help make your environment a cleaner, greener place.

1. Use less paper and always buy recycled paper products. Encourage your school or college to do so too. Ancient forests are being destroyed to make way for tree factories for the paper industry.
2. Refuse unnecessary packaging; reuse things like envelopes, bags and containers; get your household to recycle as much as possible. If there aren't enough recycling facilities ask your Council for more. We throw away 27 million tonnes of rubbish from our homes every year in the UK.
3. Take showers instead of baths. Use your washing-up water on your plants! Write to your water company urging them to stop wasting water. Rocketing demand for water is putting severe pressure on important wildlife habitats.
4. Walk, cycle and use public transport whenever possible. Let your MP know you want him/her to support measures to reduce traffic. Every year up to 24,000 people in the UK die prematurely because of air pollution, mainly due to traffic fumes.
5. Get your household to replace its three most-used light bulbs with low-energy, compact fluorescent light bulbs. Write to the company that supplies your electricity asking what they are doing to develop cleaner energy sources and help your household save energy. The energy we use at home causes more than a quarter of the UK's climate-changing carbon dioxide pollution.

Friends of the Earth

- is one of the largest international environmental networks in the world, with over 50 groups across five continents.
- is one of the UK's most influential national environmental pressure groups.
- is a unique network of campaigning local groups, working in over 200 communities throughout England, Wales and Northern Ireland.
- is dependent on individual supporters for over 90 per cent of its income.

Friends of the Earth exists to protect and improve the conditions for life on Earth, now and for the future.

© Friends of the Earth

Climate change demands action

A lack of absolute proof of human culpability over global warming does not mean that nothing should be done

By Oliver Tickell

Britain's rainiest autumn since records began 150 years ago; warm water fish washing up on Britain's shores and caught in fishermen's nets; open water at the North Pole; melting Alpine glaciers and collapsing ice caps; increased gales, storms and hurricanes; rising sea levels and more sea floods; dying coral reefs; the 10 hottest years of the 20th century all within its last 15 years . . . Do these various events prove that global warming is really happening?

On their own, no. But taken together, they make a powerful case – all the more so for being entirely consistent with the predictions of climate scientists. But it falls short of absolute proof. The climate is quite capable of changing all on its own, with no help from humans. 220,000 years ago, for example, southern England was covered in a lush, temperate forest several degrees warmer than today.

Among the influences affecting climate are eccentricities in the rotation of the Earth around the sun; wobbles in the Earth's axis of rotation; cyclical variations in the thermal output of the sun; volcanic explosions releasing huge clouds of reflective dust and sulphuric acid; vast eruptions of methane (a greenhouse gas 30 times more powerful than carbon dioxide) from the seabed; and Earth strikes by stray asteroids or comets. Then there are the chaotic fluctuations that arise from the sheer complexity of the Earths climate system and its myriad feedback loops.

The difficulty in proving the case for human-induced global warming is to distinguish the changes in climate which we experience and measure from the changes that would have taken place without our interference. Currently the only way to answer such questions is by running complex computer models, but even that falls short of the 'proof' demanded of climate sceptics.

The bottom line is we will probably never have absolute proof. Instead we would be wise to proceed on the basis of probabilities, risks and benefits. The probability is that we are causing global warming. The risk is that if we do nothing to constrain emissions, the world will be an increasingly bleak and hostile place. The benefit is that even if global warming turns out to be a chimera, the changes we should be making to combat global warming are almost all beneficial in their own right.

The UK's Hadley Centre predicts that if no action is taken, average temperatures will be 4.4°C higher by 2100, coastlines and estuaries will be taken over by the sea, flooding out 100 million people, 3.5 million square kilometres of forest will burn or die back, and three billion people will live under severe water stress. Countless species will become extinct.

By generating energy cleanly and using that energy more efficiently, on the other hand, millions of new jobs will be created, pollution of all kinds will be cut, and the Earth's finite resources will be conserved for future generations. By transferring clean technologies to developing countries, we will lift billions of people out of poverty. Reforestation could provide valuable habitats for endangered species. And the spirit of global co-operation would leave humanity better equipped to deal with other unforeseen threats that might arise.

Global warming

The term 'global warming' describes the general warming of our planet resulting from human emissions of greenhouse gases. These allow high-frequency heat-bearing solar radiation to enter the atmosphere, while reflecting or absorbing the lower-frequency thermal radiation given off by the Earth. These gases – principally water vapour, carbon dioxide and methane – are vital to maintain the Earth at a good temperature for life. But due to our burning of fossil fuels and the destruction of forests and other ecosystems, the amount of carbon dioxide in particular is growing fast. A few hundred years ago it was present at 270-280 parts per million (ppm); now it is present at 370ppm, the highest for roughly 20 million years. The vast majority of climate scientists believes that it is this level of greenhouse gases that is leading to an already discernible warming trend. According to the Hadley Centre, many of the worst effects of climate change could be avoided by stabilising carbon dioxide levels at 550ppm. To meet this target, Britain would need to cut 60 per cent off its present carbon dioxide emissions.

Going up in smoke

Little action will be taken to combat climate change while oppositions offer people an excuse to do nothing

By Polly Toynbee

Yesterday Michael Portillo inadvertently raised the key question of the century. Can western democracies ever deliver the politics necessary to save the world? To stop global warming as it is now – just to halt it – world emissions of carbon dioxide have to be cut by between 60% and 80% according to the intergovernmental panel on climate change: targets set at Kyoto which some countries won't reach were a pathetically modest first step. But outside wartime, no democracy has ever asked its voters for such savage belt-tightening or such radical lifestyle change as would be required to get anywhere near that goal.

Will it have to wait until citizens can see for themselves that climate change threatens them now, not in the future? Dying polar bears, water at the north pole, fires blazing across great tracts of land or even tropical diseases like West Nile fever breaking out in Boston make interesting newspaper stories, but they don't scare the people into a wartime frame of mind: presumably that will take water flooding over the spire of the Empire State Building.

Michael Portillo yesterday said the Conservatives would abolish Labour's climate-change levy, a pollution tax that after three years of negotiation finally comes into force in April. It will create energy savings worth about a third of the Kyoto cuts Britain has to make in carbon emissions. It is not draconian, adding only 0.45p per unit to business energy bills. It will raise £1.1bn, all of it to be recycled back to business. (It is not a Treasury money-maker). All employers will get the money back as a reduction in National Insurance contributions they pay for employees. The idea is an incentive to cut energy use, coupled with an incentive to employ more people. Ten per cent of it will be used for energy saving capital grants for business.

This policy was led by Lord Marshall, then head of the CBI. It has undergone years of delicate negotiation to ensure it is fair. Industry persuaded Gordon Brown to halve the size of his original levy, making special agreements for 80% rebates for sectors that use vast quantities of energy but employ few people – steel, chemicals, engineering. Yesterday John Cridland, deputy director-general of the CBI, said it was not opposing the climate-change levy.

The one and only supporter of Portillo's surprise announcement was the Institute of Directors. (Small business stands to gain from the NI cuts.) Portillo's rousing rhetoric at the breakfast for business included these thoughts: 'There is no justification for an energy tax which is going to be particularly harmful to manufacturing industry. Business can no longer be the fall guy.' He called the idea of taxing manufacturing industry 'ill-conceived', 'counter-productive' and 'crazy'. (Both he and the institute talked of manufacturing industry's dire plight due to the high pound, apparently shameless about their own part in Britain's failure to join the euro and rescue British manufacturing).

But most important of all, Michael Portillo took no account of global warming. He simply criticised the levy as a tax on business. It is politics as usual, no change. At least, unlike the Republicans in America, the Conservatives don't deny the existence of global warming, nor the need to do something about it. But as oppositions do and always will, they deny the need for a particular belt-tightening measure the government of the day proposes. It's 'crazy', needless, could be done better or in any other way but the one proposed. There will be a great array of methods governments choose to apply carrots and sticks to drive down energy use to hit their targets. But if oppositions always offer the people an excuse for not doing it, a reason for voting against any particular tax, quota or limit, nothing will be done.

Portillo's 'alternative' suggestion is typical weaselling. Instead of a tax, he said, his party would introduce 'emissions trading' whereby companies are given carbon quotas they can buy and sell. It gives them a financial incentive for switching to more expensive clean energy sources

such as wind or solar power that fall outside the quota. Good idea. Except that the government is already planning to do this and has a taskforce in place drawing up just such a scheme. So is the EU. But it will be needed side by side with, not instead of, a climate-change levy because it wouldn't work without that incentive. It will take several years to introduce, during which time Portillo proposes nothing should be done. The danger is that in democracies people are easily seduced by apparently pain-free alternatives offered by oppositions, ensuring governments never quite dare take measures as tough as they know they should be to hit their targets. And that's the way the world ends.

Consider the sort of lifestyle change we in the west will have to make to meet the 60-80% cut: a one-way flight from London to Miami uses up half the carbon emission a person would be allocated for a whole year's heating, cooking and transport. Will it require authoritarian national governments to introduce those kinds of severe changes, or can oppositions behave more responsibly and sit down with governments to agree global-warming measures? The

Conservatives' desperate thrashing around at the moment for any vote-catcher, however disgraceful, doesn't bode well.

To stop global warming as it is now – just to halt it – world emissions of carbon dioxide have to be cut by between 60% and 80%

Must it all be hard sacrifice? There's always a glint in the eye of the Greens that suggests they really relish anti-materialist, back-to-nature lifestyle cuts as a puritanical good thing in its own right. However, it is possible that a mixture of good government and new technology will mean nothing too drastic has to hit general standards of living. But as Michael Portillo must know, the longer action is delayed, the harsher the cuts that will need to be made later.

The climate-change levy is an excellent tool to start large energy users thinking again about ways to

convert their supplies to clean sources and to use less. For example, it will tip the balance in making it financially worthwhile for a new office building to invest in solar panels as a cladding that would give the building 30 years' free electricity at no greater construction cost than most ornamental but useless cladding. (It looks like blue marble.) The levy would tip the balance in encouraging any large energy user to invest in solar panels. The government is to use 10% of the levy for grants to help companies install this and other clean electricity supplies.

The difference in cost between clean and dirty electricity is shrinking all the time, so that relatively small extra taxes can change energy use dramatically. How high do oil prices rise before electric cars look attractive? Maybe we shall fly less often, but then trains will improve to take up the international long-distance trade. But carrots and sticks will have to start the whole process. And oppositions that try to capitalise shamelessly on what all responsible governments must do deserve to be kept out of office indefinitely.

What will the world be like in five years' time?

Professor Jim Briden, Director, Environmental Change Institute, University of Oxford, asks what scientists will achieve

In five years' time our world will be different. We'll all be older and hopefully a little wiser. And pressing climate change issues will still be with us. But what will scientists and technologists have achieved in the intervening years? What will be the challenges in developing the energy-efficient technologies needed to reduce carbon dioxide emissions?

By looking at recent developments in the UK and elsewhere, we can confidently predict that public attitudes towards government sus-

tainability policies will have been expressed at the ballot box, and perhaps even in the streets. The UK has had a recently unprecedented 'fuel crisis' as truck drivers and other road users protested against partly environmental taxes. Within the past year, international demonstrators have protested in Seattle against the globalisation policies of the WTO, and in Prague to the IMF and the World Bank. Climate change demands global policies and global action – the purpose of COP6 and the Kyoto Protocol.

The eight years since the 1992 United Nations Biodiversity Summit in Rio have demonstrated spectacularly what governments around the world can do individually and collaboratively to tackle the unprecedented problem of global change. But we also have some pointers as to what cannot be done by this top-down approach to policy implementation. We have learnt that society does not adopt sustainable practices and innovative technology through legislation alone. For a sustainable future, success or failure lies as much in the hands of society as in governments and their legislation. In Europe, 70% of housing does not have a single energy-efficient light bulb yet they benefit the householder by reducing their electricity bills.

In the search for a lower-carbon future, science, business, and industry occupy the territory linking government and citizen. They innovate the technology and services that can achieve sustainability through the consumer market place. There is ample evidence in universities around the world and at the technology exhibition currently at COP6 of an abundance of innovation both for moderation of carbon dioxide outputs and for adaptation to climate change. Acceptance of sustainable technology into the market place and conquering the risks of climate change call for the development of new relationships between business, industry, innovative universities and consumers. Sustainable technology needs more than innovative ideas. It requires public dialogue to transform society towards an energy-efficient market place and to produce lasting climate change solutions.

The world is currently short of the types of organisations, mechanisms and representative groups that are likely to be required for this change of mind-set. So just as universities have a role in technological innovation and solving of environmental problems, we also have a developing role in awareness and communication. Not only do universities need improved links with technologists and businesses; we also want dialogue with society and citizens.

Scientists and society alike have to realise that the benefits of responding to global change are not only altruistic towards future generations. The adoption of sustainable technology often brings immediate advantages in convenience, product quality, and finance. World-class universities like Oxford have a developing role as centres of impartial dialogue linking innovation, solution technology, and wider society. Science and society needs to move forward with this process, and we need to find the mechanisms for this sea change to happen. Sustainable technology might then become a lasting solution to moderating climate change. Without societal support and acceptance, 'sustainable technology' will remain a phrase for innovation without customers.

Are we to blame for this?

By Robert Matthews,
Science Correspondent

What links the following: tornadoes in Sussex, the worst floods in England for more than half a century, and the highest global temperatures since records began?

The Government at least seems in little doubt. John Prescott, the Deputy Prime Minister, told the Commons that the devastating weather of the past few weeks is a 'wake-up call to everyone' over global warming.

It is a wake-up call that many environmentalists insist is long overdue. Since the late 1980s, they have been claiming that everything from melting glaciers in Iceland to vanishing coral in the Caribbean and Indian Ocean points to the same awful conclusion: that the Earth is over-heating – and it's all our fault.

Last week, Tony Blair told a a crowd of Worcestershire flood victims of his concern that they might have been victims of global warming. On the face of it, such suspicions seem well founded. Some of those communities now under water were inundated in appalling floods barely two years ago. Add in the storms that have lashed Britain over the past decade and the predictions that global warming would mean more extreme weather, and the argument seems rock solid.

No sooner had the Prime Minister voiced his suspicions, however, than climate scientists were warning of the dangers of seeing patterns in the British climate that don't exist.

Researchers from the universities of Newcastle and Exeter unveiled a record of British rainfall dating back to the Norman Conquest. It showed that the bizarre weather of the past few years is entirely consistent with the natural variations in the climate that have taken place over the past 1,000 years.

Yet environmentalists argue that events in Britain are only part of the picture, and point to recent storms in Taiwan, floods in Bangladesh and fires in the United States as further evidence for global warming.

Even so, the scientific consensus – as expressed recently by the UN Intergovernmental Panel on Climate Change (IPCC) – is that the world's weather has not become significantly more extreme during the past 100 years.

What most scientists do accept is that the Earth is warming up: temperature records from around the world point to the 1990s as being by far the hottest decade of the century. Many scientists also insist that the chief cause of this warming is the rising level of carbon dioxide (CO_2) in the atmosphere, generated by burning fossil fuels such as coal and petrol.

The solution to global warming would thus seem clear: dramatic cuts in fossil-fuel emissions. Finalising the nature of those cuts will be the purpose of of an international meeting in The Hague later this month.

The science behind the proposed cuts is, however, far from finalised. Not everyone agrees on how big a cut is needed, how it should be effected, or whether it would do more harm than good.

Some scientists argue that global warming will lead to more extreme weather – worse floods and stronger winds, for example – essentially because, if any gas is heated, it becomes less stable. During the past five years, however, climate experts have found that all the 'filth' that industry puts into the air along with CO_2 actually combats global warming by reflecting the Sun's heat back into space.

While the precise effect of these so-called aerosols on global warming is still hotly debated, some climate experts think it might even cancel out the warming effect caused by greenhouse gases.

If true, this would have profound implications for those trying to decide how to combat global warming. The demand for a clean-up from industry might actually accelerate global warming, with who knows what consequences.

It is a possibility that has prompted one leading climate researcher to call for a shift away from controls on CO_2 and towards controls on methane, a potent greenhouse gas generated largely in the wetlands and rice paddies of developing nations.

It is a call all the more striking given that it comes from Dr James Hansen of the US Goddard Institute for Space Studies, the scientist credited with putting climate change on the political agenda in June 1988, when he told Congress: 'It is time to stop waffling so much' and accept the reality of global warming.

Dr Hansen now argues that industrialisation might not, in fact, be the source of all climatic evil. In highlighting the role of methane, he has also focused attention on the role of the Third World in combating global warming – a highly politically incorrect move that could lead to Dr Hansen's reputation among eco-warriors sinking from hero to zero.

While the arguments continue over who is to blame and who should pay, some scientists question the very notion that humans are even responsible for global warming. Instead, they point the finger of blame at the most obvious potential culprit: the Sun.

Attempts to implicate the Sun have repeatedly been howled down by climate experts, but refuse to go away. Earlier this year, a meeting of space scientists sponsored by the EU was told of a striking correlation between the temperature of the Earth and the strength of the Sun's magnetic field. The correlation stretches back more than a century, and suggests that about half of the measured global warming might have been caused by the Sun.

The solution to global warming would thus seem clear: dramatic cuts in fossil-fuel emissions

---

While many climate researchers dismiss the correlation as a statistical quirk, space scientists are taking it seriously. One explanation, put forward in 1997 by Dr Henrik Svensmark of the Danish Space Research Institute, is that the changes in magnetic field alter the levels of cosmic rays reaching the Earth's atmosphere. According to Dr Svensmark, cosmic rays might trigger cloud formation, and thus change the amount of solar heat that reaches the Earth's surface.

Satellite images of the Earth taken between 1978 and 1996 do suggest a link between cosmic ray levels and cloud cover. Whether the link is coincidence is about to be tested in experiments at Cern, the European centre for particle research in Geneva.

As with the cooling effect of aerosols, it is only in the past few years that climate experts have begun to take seriously the potential role of the Sun in global warming. Yet, once again, it could have major implications for attempts to stem climate change.

The biggest problem facing climate researchers is that they still lack computer models sophisticated enough to predict the Earth's climate with any certainty. Nothing shows this more clearly than the IPCC's estimate for the most basic figure in the global-warming debate: the likely rise in temperature in the next 100 years.

Five years ago, the IPCC forecast a rise in the range of 1.5°C to 3.5°C. In most scientific disciplines, the range of uncertainty shrinks with time as more data and insight accumulates. With climate scientists discovering only ever more complexity, the IPCC's next report

is set to forecast a rise of anywhere between 1°C and 6°C – more than double the uncertainty of five years ago.

With so little certainty surrounding so basic a figure, precise predictions of the impact of global warming on specific countries are still years away. Even so, broad-brush pictures are emerging – and, once again, they confound simplistic views of climate change.

Of all the unspoken assumptions about global warming, none is more pervasive than the view that it will visit untold misery on the Earth.

According to a study published last week of the possible effects on European countries, however, the truth is likely to be different.

The European Acacia study suggests that, while some parts of southern Europe could become intolerably arid, Britain and other northern European countries could see their climates improve, with better summers, milder winters and longer growing seasons.

Because predictions of even world-scale effects of climate change are still far from certain, any regional forecasts must be treated with caution. Nevertheless, this latest study highlights the dangers of presuming that one global climate change policy will fit all.

In the end, it hardly matters whether last week's floods were the result of man-made pollution, an overheating Sun or just the vagaries of the British climate. The real challenge facing scientists and politicians lies in doing what humans have always done: using their ingenuity to find ways of enjoying the advantages of a changing climate, while ducking its disadvantages.

Grim forecast, warns climate report

By Paul Brown and Peter Capella in Geneva

Impacts of climate change will be far worse than previously thought and beyond the capacity of mankind to adapt unless greenhouse gas emissions cut substantially, 700 scientists say in a report published yesterday.

Loss of food crops, disappearance of fisheries, melting of glaciers which provide millions of people with summer water supply, and a rise in sea levels will cause massive economic disruption and migration, it says.

The Arctic, which is already known to be suffering ice loss, could be completely ice-free in summer and the melting giant ice cap on Greenland may cause faster sea-level rise than previously thought.

Africa will be worst hit, forcing people off the land in ever greater numbers, and creating the possibility of millions of people migrating to survive. Europe, where rainfall will be plentiful – so much so that it will cause regular flooding of the type seen this winter in Britain – will increasingly be seen as the promised land for people in Africa and the Middle East.

The Intergovernmental Panel on Climate Change report is intended to guide politicians on problems they face as temperatures rise. Yesterday's assessments mean the world is heading for disasters on an unprecedented scale.

'Climate change, amongst other issues, threatens basic human needs of food, clean water and a healthy environment,' said Robert Watson, co-chairman of the report.

James MacCarthy, the second co-chairman, said some temperate countries might gain because of increased crops and faster tree growth, but others would lose.

'How much more evidence do we need before governments take real action to tackle climate change?'

Scientists have documented links between climate change and impacts in over 420 habitats. Already alpine plants in Europe are moving between three and 12ft higher each decade.

Africa was 'highly vulnerable', with climate change affecting water resources and food production, expanding deserts and causing more frequent outbreaks of diseases such as cholera. Glaciers in the mountain ranges of tropical regions were also threatened.

Himalayan glaciers, for example, are the main source of water for the Ganges and Indus on which 500m people depend. If they disappear, so does the summer water supply. John Prescott, deputy prime minister, who took part in the failed climate talks at The Hague last November, said every effort must be made to restart the negotiations and begin cutting greenhouse gas emissions.

'The new report shows that we risk major irreversible changes unless we significantly cut emissions of greenhouse gases,' he said.

'How much more evidence do we need before governments take real action to tackle climate change?' asked Russell Marsh, WWF climate change campaigner. 'The UK government should take a lead at the G8 summit and use its special relationship with the US to secure their participation in solutions to the problem of climate change.'

ADDITIONAL RESOURCES

You might like to contact the following organisations for further information. Due to the increasing cost of postage, many organisations cannot respond to enquiries unless they receive a stamped, addressed envelope.

Atmospheric Research & Information Centre (ARIC)
Department of Environmental and Geographical Sciences
Manchester Metropolitan University
Manchester, M1 5GD
Tel: 0161 247 1592
Fax: 0161 247 6332
E-mail: aric@mmu.ac.uk
Web site: www.doc.mmu.ac.uk/aric
Runs education and information programmes for air quality, acid rain and global climate change.

Friends of the Earth (FOE)
26-28 Underwood Street
London, N1 7JQ
Tel: 020 7490 1555
Fax: 020 7490 0881
E-mail: info@foe.co.uk
Web site: www.foe.co.uk
As an independent environmental group, Friends of the Earth publishes a comprehensive range of leaflets, books and in-depth briefings and reports.

Greenpeace
Canonbury Villas
London, N1 2PN
Tel: 020 7865 8100
Fax: 020 7865 8200
E-mail: gn-info@uk.greenpeace.org
Web site: www.greenpeace.org.uk
Protects the environment through peaceful direct action. Actions on land and sea against whaling, nuclear power, air and water pollution and the exploitation of wildlife.

Hadley Centre for Climate Prediction and Research
Met Office
London Road
Bracknell
Berkshire, RG12 2SY
Tel: 0845 300 300
E-mail: hadleycentre@meto.gov.uk
Web site: www.met-office.gov.uk/research/hadleycentre/index.html
Provides the United Kingdom with an up-to-date expert assessment of natural and anthropogenic changes in global and regional climate.

Royal Society for the Protection of Birds (RSPB)
The Lodge, Sandy
Bedfordshire, SG19 2DL
Tel: 01767 680551
Fax: 01767 692365
E-mail: education@rspb.org.uk
Web site: www.rspb.org.uk
The RSPB is the charity that takes action for wild birds and the environment. Produces *Sixth Sense*, a termly newsletter which is sent to all 6th form colleges and schools with 6th forms.

The John Ray Initiative
Cheltenham & Gloucester College of H.E., Room TC103
Cheltenham , GL50 4AZ
Tel: 01242 543580
Fax: 01242 532997
E-mail: jri@chelt.ac.uk
Web site: www.jri.org.uk
Works to bring together scientific and Christian understandings of the environment in a way that can be widely communicated through courses and educational materials, and lead to effective action.

United Nations Environmental Programme (UNEP)
Information Unit on Climate Change
C.P. 356
Geneva, Switzerland
Tel: + 41 22 9799242
Fax: + 41 22 797 3464
Web site: www.unep.org
UNEP works to provide leadership and encourage partnership in caring for the environment.

Worldwatch Institute
1776 Massachusetts Ave., N.W.
Washington, DC 20036-1904, USA
Tel: + 1 202 452 1999
Fax: + 1 202 296 7365
worldwatch@worldwatch.org
Web site: www.worldwatch.org
The Institute is dedicated to fostering the evolution of an environmentally sustainable society – one in which human needs are met in ways that do not threaten the health of the natural environment.

World Conservation Monitoring Centre (WCMC)
219 Huntingdon Road
Cambridge, CB3 0DL
Tel: 01223 277314
Fax: 01223 277136
E-mail: info@wcmc.org.uk
Web site: www.unep-wcmc.org
The UNEP World Conservation Monitoring Centre provides information for policy and action to conserve the living world. Now an office of the UN based in Cambridge, UK, the Centre's work is an integral part of the United Nations Environment Programme (UNEP), headquartered in Nairobi, Kenya. For information enquiries call 01223 277722.

WWF-UK
Panda House, Weyside Park
Godalming
Surrey, GU7 1XR
Tel: 01483 426444
Fax: 01483 426409
E-mail: wwf-uk@wwf-uk.org
Web site: www.wwf-uk.org
WWF-UK is the British arm of the largest independent international conservation organisation in the world. WWF works with government, industry, media and the public to protect the decline in animal and plant species and reduce pollution. WWF is committed to saving threatened wildlife species and their habitats.

Young People's Trust for the Environment and Nature Conservation (YPTENC)
8 Leapale Road
Guildford
Surrey, GU1 4JX
Tel: 01483 539600
Fax: 01483 301992
E-mail: info@yptenc.org.uk
Web site: www.yptenc.org.uk
Works to educate young people in matters relating to the conservation of the world's wild places and natural resources. Produces publications.

INDEX

★ ★ ★ ★ ★

The Internet has been likened to shopping in a supermarket without aisles. The press of a button on a Web browser can bring up thousands of sites but working your way through them to find what you want can involve long and frustrating on-line searches.

And unfortunately many sites contain inaccurate, misleading or heavily biased information. Our researchers have therefore undertaken an extensive analysis to bring you a selection of quality Web site addresses.

Greenpeace
www.greenpeace.org.uk
Go to Climate Protection on the pull down menu, then click on Global Warming and the fight to protect our climate. More detailed reports are indicated here.

Royal Society for the Protection of Birds (RSPB)
www.rspb.org.uk
Click on Conservation Issues or alternatively do a search using the key phrases 'climate change' and 'global warming'.

United Nations Environmental Programme (UNEP)
www.unep.org
Environmental issues looked at under many headings. Select a topic from the drag down menu and click on State of the Global Environment.

Hadley Centre for Climate Prediction and Research
www.met-office.gov.uk/research/hadleycentre/index.html
For the latest information about changes in global and regional climate plus further links to other sites, the Hadley Centre is worth a visit.

Worldwatch Institute
www.worldwatch.org
A great web site with an abundance of information. Their magazine *Global Eye* can also be viewed.

WWF-UK
www.wwf-uk.org
Has factsheets on climate change which look at the causes and effects of global warming and ways to reduce the threat of climate change.

ACKNOWLEDGEMENTS

The publisher is grateful for permission to reproduce the following material.

While every care has been taken to trace and acknowledge copyright, the publisher tenders its apology for any accidental infringement or where copyright has proved untraceable. The publisher would be pleased to come to a suitable arrangement in any such case with the rightful owner.

Chapter One: An Overview

Introduction to climate change, © Atmospheric Research & Information Centre (ARIC), All you ever wanted to know about climate change, © New Scientist, RBI Limited 2001, Global warming, © New Scientist, RBI Limited 2001, A greenhouse timeline, © New Scientist, RBI Limited 2001, Global warming: full steam ahead, © Guardian Newspapers Limited 2001.

Chapter Two: The Effects

Climate change, © Greenpeace, Global warming, © Young People's Trust for the Environment (YPTENC), A world of extremes as the planet hots up, © Guardian Newspapers Limited 2001, Global surface temperatures, © Crown copyright is reproduced with the permission of the Controller of Her Majesty's Stationery Office, The ozone layer, © Young People's Trust for the Environment (YPTENC), The impact of climate change on the UK, © Friends of the Earth, Biodiversity and climate change, © UNEP-WCMC, Carbon emissions per person in 2000, © Friends of the Earth International, Wet Britain, warm world, © Crown copyright is reproduced with the permission of the Controller of Her Majesty's Stationery Office, Fast facts, © Climate Voice/WWF International, Melting of earth's ice cover reaches new high, © Worldwatch Institute, Selected examples of ice melt around the world, © Worldwatch Institute, Research should not be dismissed by sceptics, © Telegraph Group Limited, London 2001, Climate change, © Crown copyright is reproduced with the permission of the Controller of Her Majesty's Stationery Office, Global warming claims 'based on false data', © Telegraph Group Limited, London 2001, World 'has not got any warmer since 1940', © Telegraph Group Limited, London 2000, The long-term outlook, © Royal Society for the Protection of Birds (RSPB), Global pollution and climate change, © The John Ray Initiative, Counting the cost of climate change, © Greenpeace.

Chapter Three: Solutions

Climate change, © WWF-UK, Climate change – the UK programme, © Crown copyright is reproduced with the permission of the Controller of Her Majesty's Stationery Office, Planet savers, © Friends of the Earth, Climate change demands action, © The Independent Newspaper Ltd 2000, Going up in smoke, © Guardian Newspapers Limited 2000, What will the world be like in five years' time?, © Guardian Newspapers Limited 2000, Are we to blame for this?, © Telegraph Group Limited, London 2000, Grim forecast, warns climate report, © Guardian Newspapers Limited 2001.

Photographs and illustrations:

Pages 1, 5, 22, 28, 32, 36: Pumpkin House, pages 4, 19, 24, 27, 31, 33, 39: Simon Kneebone.

Craig Donnellan
Cambridge
April, 2001